THIS LITTLE PLANET

This book is a product of the cooperation between the National Presbyterian Center and the Episcopal Cathedral in Washington.

THIS LITTLE PLANET

edited by Michael Hamilton

with an introduction by Edmund S. Muskie

Charles Scribner's Sons/ New York

Portions of the above essay were first published in slightly different form in *A Theology of Things* by Conrad Bonifazi. Copyright © 1967 by Conrad Bonifazi. Reprinted by permission of J. B. Lippincott Company.

A-9.70[H]

Printed in the United States of America
Library of Congress Catalog Card Number 76-120363

CONTENTS

PREFACE

by Canon Michael Hamilton

The ecological state of our planet is in disarray and is worsening day by day. The air and water are polluted, parts of our land are being poisoned; the earth is no longer able to support a number of its living species, and these conditions are adversely affecting the health of mankind. Unless we can achieve a major improvement in the conservation of our natural resources, we face the prospect of human suffering on a vast scale. Unfortunately, statements concerning this crisis fail to engender much response from the citizenry whose political support is required to change the trend. In addition to acquiring useful information, people need their emotions and spirits aroused in order to understand an issue. They need to know in detail of the plight of their neighbors, to have institutional and personal greed identified, and also to have a measure of hope offered to them that the technical problems involved can actually be solved—then they will exert themselves to seek effective legislative curbs. The problems outlined in these pages are truly horrendous; in understanding them, I hope the reader will resolve to take an active role in their solution.

The idea for this book resulted from reading a lecture of Professor Lynn White of the University of California in Los Angeles entitled "The Historical Roots of Our Ecological Crisis" (*Science,* March 10, 1967, Vol. 155, No. 3767, pp. 1203–1207). In it I was stunned by the author's criticism of the Judaeo-Christian tradition, for he argued that it encouraged the desecration of our world and the exploitation of its riches and beauty. While many of us churchmen were worried about pollution and were willing to accept our share of personal responsibility for damage, I wager few of us saw any cause to apologize for our religious faith as contributing to the problem. Professor White, on the other hand, condemned the commonly held Christian attitude toward nature as a creation of God, inferior in value to man, who was ordained to dominate it for his own gain. He argued that such belief encouraged man to misuse his environment.

My own consequent disillusionment and humiliation bred by Professor White's article led me to speculate, first, whether this prevalent religious attitude was the only one available within the Judaeo-Christian tradition. Or was it possibly a false reading of the traditional material about nature in the Old and New Testaments?

I was fortunate in being able to communicate both my gloom and hope to Dr. Lowell Ditzen, Director of the National Presbyterian Center, and together we planned a course of action for me to follow. I then set out to find theologians who would not only keep Professor White's criticism in mind, or refer to it directly, as Conrad Bonifazi has done in his chapter, but who would also search our religious heritage for whatever ethical wisdom it might have to offer to the problems engendered by man's carelessness and technology's powers. What positive ideas for conservation might be lying unrecognized within our Biblical and theological tradition which could provide understanding of and motivation for correction? This is a large task, and I am under no illusion that this book will offer more than a beginning to the treatment of the subject. Perhaps it will stimulate others to pursue the work further.

Theologians tend to fall into the trap of those whose learning is concentrated in one discipline and who are "doing their thing" without reference to what is going on in the world around them. I believe that the most useful theological thinking in recent years has emerged from people who have been personally involved in some secular issue. This bias has led me to a methodology for the book. Thus pollution, scarcity, and conservation—three central aspects of the problem of ecology which afflict the human race—were chosen, and I invited three scientists of stature to write summary articles about them. These chapters are authoritative treatments of the important conservation themes. Next I searched for three Christian thinkers each of whom had shown competence and imagination in his work and who was interested in responding to one of the scientists. In the resulting format, a scientist sets forth the nature and dimensions of the problem, with the theologian building his response, if not with scientific material, at least with his eye upon the scientist's structure.

If the theologian does his best work in response to events that are occurring outside of his professional discipline, then also the scientist today is learning that his enterprise cannot, so to speak, stand on its own feet. Neither science nor technology contain within themselves the values needed by society to use their discoveries and powers. The most obvious example is that of the physicists whose work led to the bombing of Hiroshima and abruptly forced them to see the connection between their professional research and human welfare. It is time the chemists, the industrial and automotive engineers and their employers, insofar as they contribute to pollution, recognize the critical ethical dimensions of their work. While the contributors to this book do not deal formally with the relation of science to religion or philosophy, all of them presume that serious ethical questions are involved in the matrix of scientific and political issues.

The role of the political process in gaining controls for conservation is crucial. Without an understanding of the dynamics of the forces for and against conservation, it is impossible to make relevant suggestions for reform. No man in Congress has had as much experience in environmental control matters or has developed as much legislation as Senator Edmund S. Muskie of Maine, Chairman of the Senate Subcommittee on Air and Water Pollution. His introduction speaks of the need for a balance between technological development and ecological welfare, outlines the significant legislation so far enacted for environmental controls in the United States, and finally offers some recommendations for the shape of our future society.

In addition to the close association with Dr. Ditzen, I am happy to make public my gratitude to Dean Francis B. Sayre of the Washington Cathedral for his encouragement in the production of this book; to Dr. William Pollard for technical advice;

and to Mrs. Irene Crouch, my secretary, who assisted in the preparation of the texts, and to others on the Cathedral staff who performed a multitude of related tasks.

The funding for this book came from three sources: from the National Presbyterian Center, with which the Washington Cathedral has a continuing relationship of co-sponsorship in conferences and other programs; from the Washington Cathedral Advance Program budget; and, finally, through the good offices of the Reverend Everett W. Francis, from the Joint Commission on The Church in Human Affairs of the Protestant Episcopal Church.

THIS LITTLE PLANET

INTRODUCTION

by Senator Edmund S. Muskie

> *. . . I would like to develop the analogy of our western civilization as a great pendulum whose speed and direction of motion through time is determined by the forces of technology and economic determinism on the one hand and the opposing forces of human ecology on the other. . . . The forces of technology and economic determinism, fired sequentially by the industrial age, the atomic age and the space age, have pushed the pendulum at an ever increasing and recently a dizzying speed. . . . We now have the knowledge, concepts and attitudes, not only to reverse this motion, but to then push the pendulum back to an equilibrium position which is favorable for human health and happiness. The unknown factor is man's will to do this.* [1]
>
> DR. ROBERT B. PLATT

Man is out of balance with his environment. Reaching only to critical environmental problems and then only on a limited basis, he has endangered himself and those who share this planet. The time has come for the whole society, its people and institutions—educational, political, and religious—to join together to avert further environmental crises and to plan for a future in which man can restore that balance which is essential to quality living.

Man and his environment require equilibrium. The critical factor in re-establishing this equilibrium will be man's will to create an environment adapted to his physical, psychological, and spiritual needs.

The role of religious thought and institutions in developing this will and in discovering motivations more compelling than material comfort or economic gain are essential to directing and sustaining the present concern about environmental quality. There have been repeated warnings about environmental threats to our survival, but it seems that the more intense the atmosphere of crisis, the more quickly concern is deadened. Man has learned to live with the constant threat of nuclear destruction, and, up to the present, has learned to exist in a polluted and crowded environment. But man may not be able to continue to coexist with a degraded environment. The threat of destruction from vile air, fouled water, and scarred landscapes may be more imminent than nuclear war.

Part of our difficulty comes from our preoccupation with the application of new technology, regardless of the consequences. The other part of our problem stems from our lack of understanding of the complex relationships between different organisms and the environment. Ecological sciences have grown very slowly relative to other fields of science. According to Dr. Platt, scientists began to study the interactions of communities of organisms about fifty years ago. Only in the past fifteen years have they looked at a total life environment system in a systematic way, and only in this decade has the public been alerted to the harmful ecological effects of technological manipulations of the environment.[2]

The scientific discoveries of this decade have confirmed anxieties about the health effects associated with indiscriminate release into the environment of pesticides, radioactivity, chemicals, and other pollutants. The public demand for environmental quality is no longer based solely on the desire to save the alligator, the wolf, or the roseate spoonbill. Man has joined the list of endangered species.

Recent legislation designed to correct this inbalance has been based on the philosophy of enhancement of environmental quality rather than single pollution control.

The Clean Air Act of 1963 provided financial assistance to state, regional, and local agencies for the creation and improvement of air-pollution control programs. The Federal Government was also authorized to take action to abate interstate air pollution. In 1965 Congress recognized that the automobile was the Nation's major source of pollution and initiated legislation which authorized the Secretary of Health, Education and Welfare to establish emission standards for automobile exhausts.

In the 1967 Air Quality Act a broadened program was enacted. The Act recognized the need for regional action in dealing with air pollution. Pursuant to that legislation the Secretary of Health, Education and Welfare is authorized to designate air quality control regions, distribute air quality criteria and control technology information, and require development of standards within these regions.

Progress in the field of water-pollution control legislation has been equally encouraging in this decade. The 1965 Water Quality Act authorized the development of water quality standards for the Nation's interstate water and established the Federal Water Pollution Control Administration to coordinate efforts at all levels of government. The Clean Waters Restoration Act of 1966 authorized the funds necessary for municipalities to meet the water quality standards anticipated as a result of the 1965 Act.

The Water Quality Improvement Act of 1969, now before the Congress, would, among other things, expand the ability of the Nation to cope with disastrous oil spills; require that the Federal Government in its direct activities as well as those activities which are licensed or permitted by the Federal Government to assure compliance with applicable water quality standards; and set sewage treatment standards for vessels.

But these measures will not be adequate. Continuous attention must be paid to environmental balance if we are to protect man as a species.

The way man reacts to that danger has long-range implications for the successful functioning of democracy in a technological age. How he reacts will be determined in large measure by his scale of values. Man has invested enormous faith in the value of scientific advancement, thinking that scientific knowledge would by itself bring material betterment, and therefore increase the sum of happiness. The ecological crisis facing the world and the violence of this age suggest the need for another measurement of progress. The quality and value of civilization will be determined by the extent to which man exists in harmony with the natural environment, instead of how completely he can subdue it.

The prospect of an unmastered technology carried to its logical conclusion gives rise to a *Brave New World* vision of future societies run for machines in which humanity is an inconvenience. Some see this kind of society not only as possible but as inevitable. To combat this despair, the nation needs a positive ethic directed toward producing a society where technology will work for a healthy environment, a society in which man can have faith in the future of man.

Surgeon General William Stewart described what should be the national goal before the Subcommittee on Air and Water Pollution:

> Being healthy is not just being unsick. Good health implies, to me, the full and enthusiastic use by the individual of his powers of self-fulfillment.
>
> Therefore, in controlling air pollution for the benefit of health, we are working toward an environment that is not only safe but conducive to good living.[3]

Churches are powerful educational forums. The pulpit may not have the breadth of the mass media, but it has a depth which is more likely to effect substantial changes in our ethical-environmental attitudes. Religious leaders can also make good use of secular forums of the media and forums which call for public participation in determining the kind of environment in which people will live.

In this decade many religious leaders have moved out of the cloister and into the street to support the civil rights movement, the organization of farm workers, the anti-poverty program and the cause of peace. It is important that these religious leaders and their institutions assume a greater role in the movement to improve our environment.

It is a cause which gathers strength not only from fear of ecological disaster, but from discontent with outdated and distorted priorities. It is worthy of the idealism of the young as well as the establishment. If the churches, drawing upon their own rich heritage, involve themselves in this search for new priorities, there is hope that our nation will achieve a quality of life conducive both to man's physical and spiritual well-being.

NOTES

1. Testimony of Dr. Robert B. Platt, Chairman of the Department of Biology at Emory University, before the Subcommittee on Air and Water Pollution on November 17, 1969.
2. Testimony of Dr. Robert B. Platt, November 17, 1969, before the Subcommittee.
3. Testimony of Surgeon General William Stewart before the Subcommittee, Volume III, "Air Pollution 1967."

POLLUTION

THE INJURED EARTH

by Professor Paul B. Sears

Man has become one of the great natural forces that are shaping the planet Earth. Its future condition will largely determine the welfare of his race. His relation to the physical environment, as to his fellow men, is a moral problem whose outcome depends not upon the instruments he has devised but how he uses them.

He must choose whether to be master or slave to his inventions; whether to ignore or respect the lessons of history, the best of religion and philosophy, the most perceptive intuition of the creative artist, and that growing knowledge of the natural world which we call science.

So far as I know, every form of religious belief involves an attempt to explain the nature of the universe in which man finds himself—its origin, operation, and meaning. Of necessity, these attempts have been based upon the experience and traditions of the cultures that formulate them, expressed in their peculiar idioms. More than that, they have challenged the deepest resources of the human mind. They make up much, if not most, of the world's great literature and art, and are basic to understanding them.

They give meaning to history; for men's actions, beyond physiological responses, depend largely upon their notions of the kind of world they live in and the sanctions that arise from those beliefs. These beliefs are immensely conservative, resisting innovation. Reinforced by the whole cultural apparatus, including its ethical imperatives, belief and action adjust reluctantly to changed conditions and new knowledge, accepting them so far as possible on *a priori* assumptions, if at all.

From the Near East and the Mediterranean regions, the Western world has inherited elements that paved the way for science, yet left it strangely unprepared for the consequences of that development. Monotheism postulated the reign of universal law, and Greece, at least for a time, the freedom of inquiry. More subtly, the Christian ideal of individual dignity implied the ultimate right of the individual to economic, political, and intellectual freedom, hard-won as these rights have been. Rome for her part transmitted a language of clarity and precision and a genius for organization.

On the other hand, the Judaeo-Christian heritage served to create a strong feeling that the earth was here to serve man, mixed curiously with the notion that it was a transient abode to be got through somehow, with future consequences of reward and punishment that had little if anything to do with man's treatment of it.

For fifteen hundred years this point of view, with its cosmogony, absorbed shocks from within and without until the age of exploration, the introduction of printing by movable type, and the inauguration of fresh methods of inquiry. Even so, it held its ground fairly well until the science of astronomy began to develop serious fissures in the traditional understanding of our planet and the universe of which it is a part.

Meanwhile, men had brought about profound changes on the surface of the earth, even with means today regarded as primitive. Economies and the empires they supported rose and fell. To explain their decay, theories as varied as the predilections of the explainers have been, and still are being advanced. Military, political, and moral reasons have been among the favorites. And though Plato, over two thousand years ago, clearly described the disintegration of the Grecian landscape following deforestation—especially erosion, desiccation, and lowered production—little attention was given to the role of environmental misuse as a major historical factor.

Staggering blows to the old beliefs about the cosmos and man's place within it came near the end of the eighteenth century as geology began to reveal the enormous vista of earth's past with evidence that changes could be explained by the slow, relentless work of forces still in operation. In 1859, Darwin added his reasons for believing that life itself was an expression of these changes, bearing within itself the signature of environment. Four years later, George Perkins Marsh, a native of Vermont, in his *Man and Nature,* published overwhelming evidence that man had become a major geological and biological force, often with disastrous results to himself.

It is interesting to compare the consequences of these two great contributions to knowledge. That of Darwin drew immediate fire because it presented an alternative to the literal meaning of the magnificent poetry of Genesis. Science was not yet too familiar a mode of thought for the majority; nor was it possible for those steeped in religious tradition to see that Darwin was investing man with a new dignity, involving a fearful challenge of responsibility. Wedded as cosmology had always been to moral imperatives, the new view seemed to undermine the whole ethical structure on which Western society rested.

Marsh's book was no less emphatic in its emphasis on man's obligation to his environment. Like Darwin, Marsh looked into the past for understanding of the present, emphasizing the mistakes man had made in his treatment of soil, water, forests, and other forms of life—a reminder of man's responsibility for his own future welfare. Marsh had written a classic. It was read and discussed, but it made no impression on the general public and, I fear, little or none on religious thought, preoccupied as that was with the seeming conflict between old beliefs and new ideas.

Furthermore, this message was lost on a people engaged in "conquering" a rich environment as rapidly as possible. At that time the resources of North America seemed boundless, and any thought of their future depletion a pipe dream. However, a few warning voices were raised. As a result, Yellowstone National Park was set up as a natural museum in 1872 instead of being opened to commercial exploitation; in 1892, President Benjamin Harrison reserved over two million acres as national forest, to which President Cleveland added some fifteen million more. But it was not until the administration of Theodore Roosevelt, a President who was familiar with the great West, that an extensive national forest and forestry program was set in motion. In this he was ably seconded by Gifford Pinchot and Arthur W. Greeley. What he accomplished in establishing nearly 150 million acres of national forests before Congress limited his powers is a remarkable story, as well as a prime example of the political problems facing a rational treatment of natural resources. Pressure for unchecked exploitation was then powerful, as it still is.

Forests have high visibility, and wood shortage registers clearly. Other forms of resource depletion are more subtle. World War I, like all modern wars, made heavy inroads on timber, minerals, and soil; exploitation of the semiarid Western lands for wheat-growing continued during the decade following that war. Concern for natural resources faded into the background during the deceptive prosperity of the 1920's. Only through the persistence of Hugh Hammond Bennett, a soil scientist from the South, was consent obtained for the publication in 1928 of an agricultural bulletin "Soil Erosion, a National Menace." The few who warned against the waste of oil and other mineral resources were largely ignored or indignantly disputed.

It took the greatest depression in American history, followed by prolonged drought, to restore concern for the conservation of natural resources. Dry farming for wheat had steadily expanded into the Western short-grass country of the Great Plains, at the expense of Midwestern and Eastern farmers who had been in distress since 1920. The Great Plains compose a semiarid region of some 363 million acres subject to recurring drought alternating with more humid conditions. Between 1924 and 1929, despite warnings by scientists familiar with the climatic hazards, about fifteen million acres were added to those already under mechanized farming. (Even as recently as 1958, conservative estimates were that between fifteen and twenty million acres of the 133 million in cropland should be retired, as subject to active wind erosion.) With the destruction of a plant cover that had persisted for millions of years in balance with a difficult environment by holding the soil in place and sustaining a food chain for animal life, the area was no longer cushioned against the inevitable return of drought. Then, with a rainfall varying between 11.8 and 35.4 inches per year and a high evaporation rate, the Great Plains entered a period of severe and prolonged drought in 1931. The resulting crop failures were compounded by severe dust storms whose effects were felt far beyond the limits of the short-grass high plains where they originated.

Tenant farmers with little or no capital and operator-owners of heavily mortgaged land had no choice but to leave, giving rise to a mass migration that was dramatized by John Steinbeck in *The Grapes of Wrath.* Between 1930 and 1935, 150,000 people left the Dust Bowl states, less than half of those who should have been removed to insure safe land use. (In Oklahoma in 1930, on farms below 175 acres in size, over 65 percent were tenant-operated; whereas on farms above that size only about 46 percent were operated by tenants, tenant-occupied farms comprising over half of the total number.)

Thus a large-scale physical disaster brought tragedy to thousands of families. During this time, caravans of rickety cars headed west toward California, piled high with whatever shabby possessions could be salvaged. Breakdowns were frequent, aggravated by the effect of sifting dust on bearings and carburetors, and even an occasional fire that destroyed vehicle and contents.

On looser soil types the physical effects of drifting material were spectacular and have not been exaggerated. Dry silt from bare fields often topped fence posts, buried farm machinery, and lay high against the windows of abandoned houses. Cultivated fields were swept clean down to plow sole. Only where the original grass cover remained was the surface intact, but it was buried in many places by dust from adjacent wheat land.

Adding to the impact of journalistic, literary, and scientific accounts of these dust storms was the visible presence of dust as far away as the Atlantic seaboard. Wind erosion on the Great Plains accomplished what concern over erosion by water (dating back to Colonial days) had not been able to do to the same degree in New England. These farms, handicapped, it is true, by thin forest soils overlying boulders, had been steadily abandoned for better prospects westward, after the opening of the Erie Canal in 1825. Yet many of the remaining Yankees stoutly insisted that these rocks kept pushing up through the earth, ignoring the burial by washed-out soil of stone fences at the bottoms of sloping fields and the increasing silting of once clear streams.

In the Southern states the evidence of soil erosion could not be so easily denied. Here the system of row crops—corn, cotton, and tobacco especially—not only left pathways for water, often running down instead of across slopes, but provided no cover during winter months. Fertile topsoil was lost by sheet erosion, and great gullies developed along the Piedmont. One of the most famous of these, in Georgia, cut to a depth of one hundred feet in fifty years.

Aroused at length, the Federal Government began to act. Under President Franklin D. Roosevelt, a Soil Erosion Service was set up in 1933, subsequently changed and enlarged to the Soil Conservation Service in 1935. Legislation got under way, and so did research. Districts were organized to permit local regulation with the aid of Federal technicians. New patterns of land management and cropping—marked by terraces, transverse plowing and strip-cropping, alternating horizontal bands of grass-cover with tilled crops on hillsides—began to develop.

To one flying over the nation at this time the sight was impressive, and would have been encouraging, except for one thing. These improvements were largely confined to places where the effects of water erosion had their highest visibility; that is, on rough terrain. The subtle effects of sheet erosion on gently rolling and fairly level land were ignored by farmers in the most productive parts of the country. From Ohio westward a rectangular grid of roads had imposed a completely artificial system of drainage upon the landscape. Instead of the original meandering streams in balance with topography, every highway ditch became a channel ready to carry away fertile topsoil in time of rain. In one county in northern Ohio a survey showed that no less than 20 percent of the farmland drained directly into these ditches.

In the rich Black Swamp in the northwestern part of the same state, deep drainage ditches followed the clearing of that flat area for agriculture. To the load of silt these have carried out into Lake Erie has been added an impressive amount of costly fertilizer, an economic loss to both land and water. In otherwise thrifty and prosperous Minnesota, the Cannon River that flows through Northfield is literally black with expensive real estate on the move during springtime high water. As is clear from these and countless other examples that could be cited, human activity has lowered the productive potential of the nation.

Unhappily, this somber truth has been masked by revolutionary developments in scientific, highly mechanized, heavily capitalized mass production in agriculture. The farm population engaged in the production of food and fiber has shrunk from its nineteenth-century majority to an estimated 5.4 percent at the present time. Since 1930, the number of farms has decreased from 6,546,000 to 3,059,000, while the average farm size has changed from 151 acres to 360 acres.

At first sight, the effect of these changes seems to be good, especially in view of the surpluses produced, even though the cost of food has risen. But closer examination gives less reason for cheer. The resulting population shifts have profoundly affected the urban problem, to be discussed later. It is the effect on the landscape as a soundly balanced and functioning system which is our concern at this point. To understand this, we must consider the moderate-sized, general farm family at its best. Good examples can be found in Denmark, Switzerland, and other parts of Western Europe. In our own country, they can still be seen in such cultural islands as those of religious groups in Pennsylvania and elsewhere whose lands have retained their fertility for generations.

On these farms there is a curious resemblance to the pattern afforded by plant and animal communities as they occur undisturbed in nature and as they have operated through the ages. So far as possible, a kind of stability through diversity of plant and animal life is maintained by a system of use and re-use of materials in place. Granting that the work involved on the family farm is strenuous and often exacting, it has a reality and challenge lacking in more specialized and completely mechanized labor. Engaging the entire family, it provides an environment and training compared to which it is hard to find any meaning in the life of juveniles in city slums, or even in the existence of those in the more privileged sectors of urban life.

Lest these comments seem too quaint and unrealistic, it should be added that the family farm can, by proper design, enjoy the benefits of modern applied science if the economic system is not loaded against it. Recalling that the small farm is under competition with large-scale, heavily capitalized, and highly mechanized operations, how constructive are these latter in relation to the national resources?

One feature of the mechanized operations is their physical separation of plant and animal industry. This interferes seriously with the economical recycling of materials and energy that has enabled natural communities to persist and improve the carrying capacity of the landscape through the millennia. Moreover, vast expanses are devoted to mass production of only one or a few crops, with yields maintained by artificial fertilizers, pesticides and, in the case of maize, herbicides to control weeds between rows—all of which are used to enhance the benefits from improved strains and methods of tillage.

Of the chemical fertilizers, availability of phosphates presents the most serious problem, since there appears to be little prospect of the other essential ones being in short supply. The Florida deposits are being rapidly depleted; it has been said that the time is not far off when the sandy soils of that state alone will have need for more than will be left. In addition, the strip mining of these deposits has left ugly scars over a wide area, but perhaps the rising value of land will eventually justify their restoration. Fortunately, there remain great reserves, largely on government land, in the Rocky Mountain states. One must hope that these will be developed primarily for the general good, rather than for excessive profits, and in a manner which will insure the most effective and frugal use for as long as possible.

Besides what it has contributed to our understanding of plant and animal nutrition, modern chemistry has endeavored to help control organisms deemed undesirable to man. Biocides include not only chemical compounds that kill disease-producing bacteria, but poisons for insects, other animals, and weeds. Along with detergents, such substances have never existed in nature; consequently, evolution has not produced organisms which can break them down into harmless or useful form as happens with most organic compounds. Furthermore, man has created the need for such materials by upsetting the balance of nature that normally keeps destructive organisms within bounds.

Biocides are seldom selective, generally killing harmless and useful forms of life as well as pests. Often they are used carelessly, increasing the danger of mishap. They are produced in vast amounts, running up to hundreds of millions of pounds annually for DDT alone. Applied by airplane, this substance drifts far beyond the target areas and is now found even in the Antarctic. Accumulating in the body fat of fishes and other animals, it causes sterility in fish-eating birds and is a prime cause of the decrease of eagles. In one area of Maryland, for example, it was responsible for a 26 percent decline in bird population. Soil residues eaten by earthworms have been responsible for a heavy toll among robins.

The ultimate effect on human health is a matter of debate, but it is significant that dairies are subject to shutdown if the DDT content of milk exceeds prescribed standards. Where aerial spraying for mosquitoes is practiced, endangering nearby pastures, this problem can be serious. Recent estimates indicate that 300 to 500 million pounds of this substance are now "floating around" in the earth's atmosphere and that an incredible amount is now present in the fatty tissues of human beings in this country. Obviously this situation calls not only for thorough and disinterested research but also for action. In some places the use of DDT is now forbidden by law. It is significant that while Rachel Carson and her book, *Silent Spring,* were still being attacked in this country the British were proceeding with remedial legislation.

Included in this legislation were orders to devise detergents that could be broken down by microorganic action and decay. Heavy doses of detergent in drainage not only produce great masses of foam in rivers and lakes but encourage heavy growth of algae whose dead bodies consume oxygen essential to fish and other aquatic animals. In Lake Erie the combination of detergents, fertilizer, and raw sewage has so depleted the oxygen supply that may-fly larvae, essential as food for bass and pickerel, have been practically eliminated.

So far as pest control is concerned, there is need for really imaginative research on the possibilities of improving it, as our mass-produced crops, grown with such efficiency, offer so rich an opportunity for epidemic pests. One study that was under way as early as 1910 has already paid off. This dealt with the search for parasites that would attack insects injurious to sugar cane. Spraying for these insects would, of course, kill any of their parasites. However, recent reports indicate that unsprayed plantations in Hawaii have been showing better results than those which were sprayed. The difficulty is that research for biological as opposed to chemical controls often requires a long period of sustained work without immediate profits. Where it is interrupted—as it often is—by government or corporate budget-cutting, a great waste of previous effort, as well as serious delay, is likely to result.

bers are a distinct advantage. This has been especially true since the beginnings of agriculture relieved some members of the group from the incessant search for food, thus allowing them leisure to develop the arts, which made possible fuller use of environmental resources.

Eventually—in recent times at an accelerated rate—the combination of human biological and cultural success approached its inexorable limit. Man is no longer his own potential competitor, but actually and tragically, his worst rival in an environment badly depleted by the very facility of his culture in exploiting it. How rapidly this convergence of breeding and depletion has become evident can be shown by the record. Serious attention to a damaged environment dates practically to the beginning of the twentieth century; anything more than token attention to population pressure began only with the baby boom following World War II. Not until the mid-1950's did the majority of conservationists begin to shift emphasis from resources to numbers.

Thus in 1967 David Brower admitted that "it was only twelve years ago that we even suggested, in any Sierra Club publication, that uncontrolled population was a menace!" How rapid was the change is shown by the fact that within two or three years, instead of early protests at the mention of the problem, he received vociferous complaints if he failed to do so.

If further evidence is needed, it is supplied by the three books of the late Fairfield Osborn through whose insight, energy, and statesmanship the Conservation Foundation was launched. His *Our Plundered Planet,* outlining man's devastation of the earth, was published in 1948. His next book, *The Limits of the Earth,* in 1953, showed the finite character of the resources needed by man, while in *Our Crowded Planet,* 1962, he edited essays by twenty-one writers whose views are expressed succinctly in the title used by Julian Huxley, "Too

Many People." In a letter written not long before his death, Dr. Osborn stated that he would be mildly optimistic regarding man's future if the population problem were solved. The Population Reference Bureau, which under Robert Cook has been one of the sanest and most effective forces for population control, was not incorporated until 1951.

The awakening interest in population pressure on the part of many whose chief concern has been on human damage to environment is now producing gloomy forecasts—not of the distant but rather the more immediate future. Coming from responsible sources, taking full account of present and prospective food production, of widespread existing hunger and malnutrition and the dim prospects for any early control of world birth rates, their statements predict major famine within the next few years.

Critics of this view include humanitarians whose argument essentially is that since the world's people should be fed, they must be fed and ergo will be. Others represent the suppliers of fertilizers, herbicides, and pesticides now used to insure high yields in advanced agricultural practice. Bolstering the optimistic view have been references to farming the oceans, watering the deserts by desalting the seas, developing the tropics, and producing synthetic foods from petroleum or by the action of microorganisms on wastes of various kinds, including sewage. In every instance where these proposals have been carefully studied, as, for example, by Paul W. Ehrlich in his *The Population Bomb,* they turn out to be inadequate at best, if not technically impractical or even absurd.

Vast expanses of ocean produce little life and are virtual deserts. Production is highest along coasts where nutrients in river mouths meet those brought in by tide, or where nutrients are brought to the surface by upswelling currents; probably such materials owe their presence on the sea bottom to wash from land. Leaving aside the matter of quantity, we are notoriously fouling the streams that flow into the seas with industrial and municipal wastes. In Connecticut, for example, revenue from shellfish has dwindled at today's prices from about $40,000,000 in 1910 to $3,000,000 in 1966. Thus instead of increasing our harvest from the seas we are actually making such an increase impossible at a time when its feasibility is being urged to justify complacency about population control.

As to the tropics, it is now clear that the combination of heat and moisture tends to render their soils unproductive when cleared for conventional agriculture. They are used to best advantage for crops grown in partial shade, such as coffee and cocoa, or where conditions favor the production of rice. Great advances are being made in increasing rice production but the unquestioned evidence of widespread hunger in the Orient shows that a world which cannot feed its present population has little chance to feed a future one being produced at a compound interest rate. Complicating this situation is a recent report that hungry rice-eaters have objected to the taste of the new, improved varieties. Lest this seem a trivial matter, we recall the rejection of American corn sent to Europe for famine relief after World War I or, less seriously, the thunderous protests of a South Carolina divine and epicure when he entered his house and caught the aroma of Louisiana rice being cooked.

Despite the great advances made in medical science and art, there is the possibility that a new and virulent epidemic might sweep the world. This could happen through the natural evolution of new pathogens from old, or, sad to say, through the escape of dangerous strains of organisms now being produced in biological warfare laboratories of the "advanced" nations. While such an epidemic would probably take its heaviest toll among those already debilitated by food shortage, there is no reason to believe that others would be immune. As human population approaches supersaturation, we cannot rule out the operation of the two ancient checks, famine and disease.

Nor is modern society any less safe from the third horseman—war. Within the present generation we have seen the technology of destruction develop to the point where it holds the power to destroy mankind. We have seen the killing of noncombatants as an adjunct to armed conflict take the form of genocide, and we have seen civil wars claim these innocent victims by the millions, as happened under Stalin and in China. Setbacks to population growth due to limited conventional warfare are usually made up by the subsequent rise in birth rates, but with the development of atomic weapons and the resurgent ruthlessness which two millennia of Christian teaching and five centuries of humanistic learning have not dispelled, modern war can easily take its place beside famine and disease in a crowded and confused world.

Whether or not it does so, the destructiveness of wars, small or large, is not confined to human lives. Besides the actual damage and wastage of fighting, the postures labeled "defense" are greedy devourers of raw materials, energy, and treasure. In half a century a mountain of iron in the Mesabi Range has been eaten away and dissipated; a nation's economy has become so specialized for and geared to military production that the advent of genuine peace would leave it gasping, despite vast domestic needs; and living costs have increased fourfold in terms of a currency that has been debased as truly as if some king had clipped his coinage.

From Vietnam there are daily reports in the news of the dropping of hundreds of tons of explosives and the use of defoliants and crop-destroying chemicals. Published photographs show pockmarked landscapes rendered sterile and unproductive, while reports as to the ecological effects of defoliants are equivocal at best. As this is being written, an agricultural scientist who has examined the damaged terrain estimates that twenty years may be required to bring it back to a useful condition. In short, war is a greedy destroyer of natural resources, consuming both human lives and the tangible assets over which the fighting goes on.

An honest appraisal of the condition of our natural resources must not only record what we have done to them in the past but must identify what is going on now that threatens further damage. Wise resource management has recently become concerned with population control; it must still further expand its concern to include support of measures to abolish war. For whatever war may do to reduce, at least temporarily, human numbers is more than matched by its ruthless destruction of basic wealth. For the sake of a future productive environment, if for no other reason, we cannot longer be passably tolerant toward the greedy belly of the war god. The Land Ethic, so beautifully presented by the late Aldo Leopold in his book, *Sand County Almanac,* must be extended to include an obligation to resume the efforts begun by American statesmen early in this century to develop effective, peaceful means for dealing with conflicts of interest among nations.

However grim and saddening the deaths from widespread famine will be, a deeper and more fundamental tragedy for our species will result if the depletion and disruption of the planetary environment continues at its present rate. There is no warrant for neglecting the traditional concern of the conservationist with environment just because of his new awareness of the population peril.

We mentioned in the beginning the innate relation between religion and world view, i.e., cosmogony (origins) and cosmology (nature), noting briefly the doctrinal stresses arising from revisions of views long held, notably exemplified by the impact of evolutionary theory on Christian fundamentalism.

To scrutinize, formulate, and dramatize the elements of a new religious ethos is a creative task of high order not to be confined to conventional ecclesiastic establishment. Into it must go the work of poet, philosopher, prophet, and pastor, as well as much of the new talent peculiar to the modern world.

At this point let us resume our examination of the consequences of man's impact, both in numbers and ways of life, on the great physical and biological system of which he is a part rather than a mere onlooker and beneficiary. We have discussed his damage to the rural landscape from which come food and fiber, and the lively threat of famine or other disasters in consequence of accelerated population growth. With over 80 percent of our population reckoned as urban and fewer than one person in ten producing food and fiber for all on the nation's farms, it is time to extend our attention to the entire landscape, with emphasis on the effects of urbanization.

Until very recently the attention of conservationists centered on the danger of depletion or destruction of natural resources, as we have noted. With such exceptions as the oil wells in Oklahoma City and on Signal Hill in San Francisco, most natural resources are not thought of as urban, at least in terms of their location. But, least of all today, neither resources nor the problem of the cities can be considered apart from the other with any profit. In fact, one of the most disappointing features of a great deal of discussion of the urban crisis is its neglect of the total environment, of which the city, however vast and sprawling, is only a portion.

In the first place, the city is the offspring of the farm; until the invention of agriculture men had to scatter out in search of food and were so busy with that search that there was little time or energy for other arts. This is one of the most reasonable deductions to be made from our knowledge of modern primitives and the evidence of archaeology.

We also have sound reasons to believe that, as cities followed the first agricultural villages and masonry replaced thatch and mud, the city served a function in relation to agriculture. It developed calendars and accumulated lore pertaining to plant and animal production. However crude such knowledge may seem to us in a scientific age, what we know of it from ancient writings that have been preserved commands respect. At any rate, it was the best to be had—not lightly to be rejected as superstition. True, it included errors; but so do the best of modern manuals. We would say today that it was largely fictionalized, lending itself to communication through song and ceremony, art and ritual—sources of some of our greatest literature and still among the most effective ways of influencing people. Smoky the Bear may not be high art, but he seems to be better at discouraging forest fires than pages of graphs and tabulated statistics.

As Newton reasoned and the astronauts have so brilliantly demonstrated, a body set in motion continues to move, subject only to the pattern of forces in the system of which it is a part. Once the city got started as an institution, assured of continuing nourishment by the conditions within human societies that made it possible in the first place, it grew in power, prestige, and diversity of the arts. It grew in size and in its demands for the products of the surrounding rural landscape. Along with this increasing appetite went an impoverishment of the soil and a lowering of the status of the farm worker. Greece became dependent upon foreign grain, Rome upon that of northern Africa. Slave farm workers replaced the yeomen of Cincinnatus and Cato.

We can infer from our diggings and from more recent records something of the way in which the inevitable wastes were handled. Garbage found ready use for feeding animals such as poultry and swine, not only on adjacent farms but within city limits so long as they were permitted there. Even in recent times American families resident in the crowded Orient have been able to get their laundry done in exchange for the night soil—urine and feces—gathered each morning and taken to pits for digestion and sale to local gardens and farms. Inorganic materials such as ceramics and stone accumulated within and around the city, representing essentially a geological process of novel character that gave rise to the tels or artificial hills dear to the modern archaeologist in his exploration of ancient city sites.

As cities in the Western world grew in size and became more sharply differentiated from the rural areas that supplied them, the nutrient relationship began to suggest that between parasite and host. Giving as little as possible, the city drew upon the countryside for all it could get, becoming a vortex so far as materials, both organic and inorganic, were concerned. With consumption there is always waste, increasing as the influx of consumables increases. The vending of food and fiber is more profitable and the demand for them more insistent than the disposal of their wastes. Not surprisingly, the medieval city was a filthy place; what could not be thrown or drained into nearby streams accumulated in the streets. Vermin that fattened on refuse often became vectors of epidemic disease, while wells contaminated with human wastes were potent sources of typhoid and other enteric ills. Only toward the end of the nineteenth century did these conditions come under control in the United States, while Japan in its war of 1903 with Russia was the first nation in modern history to lose fewer men by disease than battle.

By the time of Elizabeth I, the scarcity of wood and availability of coal had added smoke to decay and other nauseous odors as a source of air pollution in England. One suspects that the famous blast of James I against tobacco may have been something more than the cranky reaction of a royal bigot. Dangerous filth persisted long after the Stuart regime as is evident in the statement of Dr. Robert S. Morison, Director of the Division of Biological Sciences at Cornell University, that John Wesley, an Anglican priest who worked among the victims of the industrial revolution, did more for public health in England than all the doctors of his day. This he accomplished by his insistent preaching that cleanliness is next to godliness.

The rapid application of science has intensified rather than changed the relation of the city to the general landscape. It is still dependent upon rural areas for its supplies and still plagued by the problem of waste disposal. Pipelines for water and fuel reach out like tentacles for increasing distances, often coming into competition with other urban centers. By water, land, and air, food and other raw materials are sucked in from lengthening radii, while water, air, and land are taxed to the limit to take care of industrial and domestic residues. To wastes which have been more or less normal since cities began and which in a rural economy are returned to the soil for its benefit are now added many forms of matter entirely new in the history of evolution and immune to bacterial breakdown. Many of these are biocides by design, others are as a side effect of their intended function; still others, like the exhaust fumes from internal combustion motors, are dangerous and unwelcomed by-products. One estimate is that 90 million automobile engines in America are now throwing off over 90 million tons of carbon monoxide a year, which, if confined to the air space above Massachusetts, Connecticut, and New Jersey, would be sufficient to poison it. Figures on the bathing beaches, for example, that have been rendered unsafe by pollution are equally impressive.

Public resentment of air and water pollution is growing; space available for landfill is increasingly scarce and expensive, as more of it is needed for other uses, including open space for wildlife and recreational purposes. Yet there are powerful obstacles in the way of reform. One is sheer expense. If Toledo, for example, were to take the first step toward cleaning up its drainage into Lake Erie, it would involve separation of storm from sanitary sewers. This would cost an estimated 80 million dollars, an amount not available. When an official of Pratt-Whitney was commended for plant design which insured clean effluent (at a reported cost of one million dollars), he replied, "You should see the letters I got castigating me for setting such a bad example to other industries." Again, when a visitor protested the nauseous odor from a plant making paper products, his host, an executive of the concern, said, "That's funny, all I can smell is bread and butter."

So far as I know no one has called ours The Age of Paper, although there is reason as good as that for speaking of the Stone and Bronze Ages. Granted that paper is impermanent, our enormous structures of steel and concrete, as well as the intricate mechanisms upon which modern technology rests, all depend for their presence upon plans, records, reports, and contracts done on paper. None of the professions could maintain their standards without the aid of vast libraries. Along with fossil fuels, metals, and other minerals, paper is one of the mainstays—in some respects a peculiarly important one—of our modern way of life.

The heaviest industrial use of water is in the fabrication of metals, chemicals, and paper. Paper mills discharge solid wastes in the form of fiber as well as soluble chemicals into streams that thus become unfit to support aquatic life. Volatile wastes that escape into the air create what are among the most unpleasant of nonlethal industrial environments. Not many decades ago, paper made up perhaps a fourth of city garbage and similar solid waste. Today, along with plastics, it makes up at least three fourths, creating one of the several problems involved in the reclamation of such wastes for soil improvement and other uses.

Metals in nature are usually in the form of compounds with oxygen, sulphur, silicon, etc. In their separation by smelting, these other elements are released into the air, affecting visibility, odor, and purity. Such deterioration of the atmosphere is no longer confined to heavily populated industrial centers; it is spreading into remote parts of the country whose clean, bracing air has been one of the main attractions to those able to escape from "civilization." The National Observatory on Kitt's Peak, Arizona, was built at that remote and lofty site for the sake of clear air. Each year since its establishment the pall of dust and fumes has risen higher from the smelters and other sources on lower lands at its base; nor are there any signs of improvement.

More widely distributed than the wastes of either the paper or metal industry are the by-products of the combustion of fossil fuels—coal, gas, and oil. In contrast to smelting, which separates the metals from other elements, burning combines carbon, sulphur, nitrogen, hydrogen, etc., with oxygen as energy is released. Among the simpler of these new compounds are water and carbon dioxide, both necessary to sustain plant life; but both can be dangerous in excess since they cannot support combustion or the oxidation that supplies energy through breathing to living bodies.

Among the other compounds, carbon monoxide is a notorious and dangerous poison. Recent studies show a higher accumulation of it in urban people (especially cigarette smokers) than in those who have better air to breathe, for the urbanites exhibit a higher incidence of emphysema and other pulmonary troubles. Still other compounds remaining in the atmosphere, or rising to the stratosphere, are reported to undergo changes that render them detrimental to life as they are returned by turbulence into the zone of breathing.

It is the prevalent opinion among scientists that the earth's supply of free oxygen came about after the evolution of plants which, using solar energy, released it as they manufactured organic materials. This has resulted in a delicate balance between oxygen (20 percent of the atmosphere) and carbon dioxide (three tenths of 1 percent) that is maintained by the interaction between green plants and all other forms of life. At present carbon is being oxidized, i.e., oxygen being bound, at a rate far above what has been normal through millions of years. What the consequences will be we do not know. Predictions are being made in good faith and by reputable authorities that a dangerous change in the heat balance of the planet—a so-called greenhouse effect—will eventually occur; other scientists anticipate an ultimate shortage of oxygen with the obvious menace to animal life. Much depends upon the chemical resilience of the oceans that cover three fourths of the earth. Sea water has a strong capacity to absorb carbon dioxide. In warm waters this combines with calcium, and vast amounts of the resulting lime are converted into coral, shell, sand, and ooze, as any skin-diver knows. In fertile spots the floating life of the sea retains the carbon and releases a net amount of oxygen. Many of these most fertile areas border the land and interchange nutrients with it. In increasing amounts, the contributions from land include silt, sewage, and industrial wastes, many of them toxic. The net effect is clear from figures on the decline of shellfish and fish yields; the long-time effect on the atmosphere remains to be seen.

Intensifying the grave problem of water pollution is the question of an adequate water supply. Since 1900, water use has increased at twice the rate of population growth, current withdrawals for all purposes now exceeding 1,300 gallons per capita per day. During the decade 1950–60, municipal demands increased by 150 percent, those of agriculture by 130 percent, and of industry, the heaviest user, by 180 percent. The fact that an amount estimated to be in excess of 75 percent is returned to surface or underground storage merely emphasizes the imperative need for controlling pollution, aside from minimizing losses by evaporation of surface waters.

The projections for 1980 are no less disturbing, for they indicate a doubling of 1960 withdrawals, or about half the total water supply that is expected, on the basis of present rainfall figures. Meanwhile, underground water, which remains an important source of supply, is being pumped out in many places faster than it is being replenished; some areas of the Southwest are actually using "fossil water" stored underground thousands of years ago and not now receiving fresh supplies.

Concern for future water supplies has stimulated active interest in desalting sea water, costly in energy as that process still is; it has also given rise to proposals for the long-distance piping of water from regions of present abundance, an idea less than welcome to the citizens of such places.

A neglected aspect of the water problem, affecting both availability for use and prevention of flood damage, is the design of land use. This involves such matters as highway location and drainage, adequate ground cover, and site selection for industrial and housing developments. Dams, too often regarded as a simple solution, may fail in their purpose if the contributing watershed is not sufficiently protected by vegetation to prevent rapid siltation of the reservoir behind them. In California, the hazard of building homes on clay terraces bulldozed on steep slopes has been evident for many years, yet it continues even to the present time, with the recent disastrous results. Matching this practice has been the toleration by municipalities elsewhere of housing developments on areas known to all except incoming house buyers to be flood plains and thus subject to periodic submergence.

There is a ground swell of concern, not only to clean up the air, rivers, and lakes but also to protect wetlands, both inland and coastal, from further destruction and pollution. Leading in this movement are national organizations of sportsmen and other protectors of wildlife habitat, supported in many cases by groups of local citizens. Beyond the inertia of public indifference, their efforts encounter strong opposition from those interests who stand to profit substantially by exploitation of these resources.

As leaven to this rather depressing report on current conditions is the considerable activity of numerous private organizations concerned with the many aspects of conservation. Also noteworthy is the concern of appropriate Congressional committees and in particular a Presidential message printed in House Document No. 47 of the 90th Congress. While dealing primarily with air pollution, the message also discusses other resource problems, including the urgent need for pure water. Deserving mention, too, are recent accomplishments of the Department of Interior and other major divisions of the Federal Government. Activities of state governments have been unequally commendable; however, if any general statement can be made here, it is that the younger the state, the greater the tendency toward exploitation. Older states tend to have a greater variety of special groups serving as watchdogs.

The growing needs of municipalities and industry for cheap waste disposal, and the fact that land areas remain limited while population continues to increase, offer ready arguments against cleaning up and preserving lakes, streams, and wetlands. The issue is often made to seem one of people vs. fish or ducks or "useless" natural areas. Even if the ethical question of respect for other forms of life is ignored, there remains the less obvious but vital question of disrupting the functioning, integrated operations that have sustained the quality of land, water, and air, and made the earth habitable for man. This, unfortunately, is a matter which does not lend itself to the dangerous oversimplification to which we have become accustomed in print, sound, and picture. Older than the Huns and Vandals and not unknown in modern warfare is the idea: "If you can't eat it, sell it or (otherwise) use it, smash it."

In economics the term "land" is a technical one, designating not only area but quality, thereby including the distribution of all resources whether on the surface or below it. Area or space is a primary resource remaining relatively fixed, while human numbers increase. On that score, the best approximations indicate that the Indian population of what is now the contiguous United States was about one million in the time of Columbus, providing roughly 2,000 acres per capita, or somewhat less than four square miles. This is about what an economy of hunting and fishing, supplemented with casual agriculture, needs. Today the same area represents about ten acres per capita. Much of this is unproductive for agriculture, while the yield of game has become relatively small and that of inland and even coastal fisheries is greatly reduced.

For a variety of reasons—including field sports and other forms of recreation, concern for wildlife as such, and sheer aesthetic interest in nature—there is growing pressure to maintain open space in the face of continuing alienation. Many uses of open land do not require it to be left in natural condition, but there are important reasons for the preservation of generous areas in as nearly a natural state as possible.

From a purely economic standpoint it is necessary to recall that native living cover has withstood the vicissitudes of climate and is adjusted to site. It has conserved land forms, developed soil, and regulated the flow of water, as well as insuring the purity of the atmosphere. My observations in all of the states convinced me some time ago that a healthily functioning landscape required something on the order of 20 to 25 percent to be in a type of cover that is a reasonable approximation of the original. It was heartening to learn later that this was the estimate made by George Perkins Marsh more than a century before.

To meet this requirement does not preclude use, so long as woodland is kept where forests once grew and mixed grass-legume cover where there had been prairie. But there are urgent reasons, aside from the purely aesthetic and ethical, important as these may be, for saving some areas in the wild condition. Natural ecosystems afford a necessary model as essential to the biologist as standards to the physical scientist if a rational pattern of land use is ever to be worked out.

Through the millennia these systems have operated on the current budget of sunshine, utilizing energy and materials in place to build up the productive capacity of the landscape. There is nothing in nature that compares with the flow of energy and materials into modern centers of population, their rising accumulation of wastes and production of toxic materials. In contrast to the constructive and stabilizing processes of world without man, this trend is ultimately a destructive one.

It is both possible and necessary for man to develop a pattern for the use of energy and materials which approximates the processes that have made the world habitable for him. But to do this we need to understand better what those processes are; for the present we have to eke out our limited understanding of natural ecosystems with a good share of intuitive judgment. To continue destroying these systems is to the ecologist what would happen to the chemist if we wrecked his laboratories.

One of the important aspects of natural systems, already noted, is the diversity and balance of their populations. This balance is maintained not only by limiting numbers but also by adjusting distribution. However harsh the means, the effect is to permit each surviving individual and group to function normally. Here in most graphic fashion the present trend of technology and urbanization does violence to the long established model of the world of nature.

During the critical period of the 1930's, there was reason

to believe that no city of any considerable size maintained its population level by its internal birth rate. In the aftermath of World War II the birth rate rose rapidly. At the same time the mechanization of agriculture displaced rural workers, *driving* as well as drawing them into the cities in numbers beyond the chances for useful employment. Meanwhile, technical improvements in the mass production of consumers' goods have tended to require less personnel per unit of production, while the refugees from a new kind of rural economy continued their high birth rate, sustained by growing allowances for relief. In some areas there is now a third generation of these immigrants that has known no other method of survival.

The problems of the modern city are too obvious to require elaboration here, taxing comparison as well as ingenuity. They involve decent housing, education, health, delinquency, and finance. The economic aspects alone were succinctly outlined in 1959 by Joseph Spengler in the *Harvard Business Review* where he demonstrated that after a city reaches its optimum size, further increase represents a liability instead of an asset. The saddest victims of this situation are the young, whatever their color, who are growing up in a world which seems not to need them and which gives them little opportunity to function as normal, active, and useful human beings.

This situation has created apprehension and, to a lesser degree, I fear, pity among the more fortunate citizenry. To the extent that they can, they escape for living, if not for work, to the suburbs for a period of respite until the expanding city overtakes them. Planners are already warning them that they must prepare to divide up their living space. Meanwhile, city administrations are calling upon planners to improve conditions within the cities. With massive aid from public funds, housing is being developed—but at a rate that lags far behind need and does little or nothing to redistribute population. Industry is making a major effort to decentralize. In some places this gives part-time employment along with some opportunity for subsistence farming and gardening to its employees. This is good. Elsewhere the effect has been to increase the financial burdens for education and other public services in what are known as dormitory towns, without equivalent financial return from the incoming workers.

Yet to be faced squarely are the enormous costs of cleaning up and, so far as possible, returning for use the effluvia—solid, liquid, and gaseous—from great centers of population. Increasingly, we have become dependent upon an elaborate technology, sensitive to mishap, lengthening the chain between man and nature, increasing our dependence upon the specialist, and obscuring the total picture. As a nation on wheels we are determining the future geometry of our landscape by incontinent building of highways, quite often laid out with no regard to the ultimate best use of land. With vast sums at their disposal, highway commissions are virtually a law unto themselves, untouchable save when the public is able to reach the ear of a sympathetic governor.

To maintain our present way of life, we have become the world's most extravagant users of fossil energy, at present consuming more than half the world's production of fuels and other minerals. Perhaps there is no better way to make clear what this means than by reminding ourselves of a firm principle of physical science that applies to dynamic particles, whether they be atoms or beings endowed with intelligence. As such units increase in number within a finite space—be that space a flask of gas, an island, or a peopled continent—so does pressure. In technical language, there is a decrease of mean free path. Then, as energy is added to the system, whether it be by heating the flask or speeding up the movement of human beings with the aid of internal combustion engines on wheels the mean free path is further constricted. And when energy is added excessively and without control, as happens to a drop of water on a hot stove, the system breaks up.

It would be the ghastliest of errors to regard the present rebellion of the world's young as a passing aberration; they are in revolt against a society whose uncontrolled use of technology—not science—is threatening the dignity of the individual, clouding the meaning of life and even the possibility of hope. To quote from the address of Don K. Price, retiring president of the American Association for the Advancement of Science, in what is by all odds one of the most significant statements ever made from that rostrum:

"The rebels are right in being pessimists ... I do not think they are pessimistic enough. To me it seems possible that the new amount of technological power let loose in an overcrowded world may overload any system we may devise for its control; the possibility of a complete and apocalyptic end of civilization cannot be dismissed as a morbid fancy."

To this let me add that several decades of study of environment and of man so inseparably bound to it have made clear to me that hope lies not in device but in design, not in technique but in the realm of the intangibles—the values and sanctions of our culture. If ever the custodians of religious faith have been challenged, they are challenged today.

GOD AND HIS CREATION

by Dr. William G. Pollard

People all over the earth have been thrilled with the beautiful pictures of our planet sent back by TV from the Apollo missions and subsequently reproduced in color from still photographs. From these we have acquired a new perspective on the earth. We realize, as we never quite did before, how small, restricted, and limited is this ball floating out in space which is our home in the universe. In addition, the Apollo pictures and mission have given us a fresh appreciation for the beauty of the earth in comparison with the moon and other planets. All of this has an importance for the history of man on this planet through the remainder of this century which few suspect. We have reached a crucial turning point in our relationship with the earth, the nature of which it is of vital importance that each of us understands.

This is quite new in human experience. Throughout the many previous centuries of man's habitation of the planet, the earth seemed a vast unending frontier of unlimited resources. On land or sea it seemed to stretch out before man without limit. In the first chapter of this book, Paul Sears rightly describes the assumptions of the pioneers who first migrated west over the face of the American continent that the land seemed almost boundless in its riches and extent. It is said that when man first appeared on the planet God said that he would "be fruitful and multiply and fill the earth and subdue it, and have dominion over the fish of the sea, and over the birds of the air, and over the cattle, and over the whole earth." (Gen. 1:26–28) In any previous century, the thought of man or anything else filling the earth would have seemed fantastic; vast areas, even whole continents, of the earth's surface were only sparsely, if at all, settled by man. Man thought consciously of himself as a minority species among many others which outnumbered him. Human settlements were for the most part tiny islands in the midst of or on the edge of the great primeval forests of the earth. Man exercised a limited dominion over horse and dog, sheep and cattle, but always there was danger and uncertainty as ever watchful tigers or wolves lurked in the shadows. Over two essential elements, the world of microorganisms and the fertility of the soil, he exercised no dominion whatever. As a result, epidemic disease, plague, and famine were ever-present threats, periodically actualized in terrible scourges before which man stood helpless. Bound as he was to the earth's surface, the birds of the air remained beyond his reach. For all his cleverness as a fisherman and sailor, the sea remained vast and alien in which creatures large and small disported themselves, oblivious of man and his ways. The dominion exercised by man was token and symbolic at best, and he was very, very far indeed from having subdued the whole earth to his purposes.

The twentieth century has changed all this. In earlier centuries man had been fruitful, but he had not multiplied appreciably. At the beginning of the Christian era there were only about 300 million human beings on the earth. It required seventeen centuries to double this number to 600 million. Then, in 1820, for the first time the world population of species *Homo sapiens* passed the one billion mark. By 1930 it had doubled to two billion. Just a few years ago, in the early 1960's it passed three billion. By 1975 it will have reached four billion. Thereafter, if present levels of human fertility and declining death rates continue, it will reach five billion by 1985, six billion by 1993, and at the end of the century, thirty years from now, it will stand at 7.2 billion. The earth will then be just twice as crowded as it is now. Moreover, man will have effectively filled it. It will have all the human beings it can support and feed at any reasonable level of quality of life.

This same century, the twentieth, is also the century in which man has first realized a full dominion over the earth and has been in the process of subduing it. There are several still living today whose childhood was spent in the first decade of this century before the advent of the automobile or the airplane, electric power, radio, and TV, and great cities and highways as we know them today. In just the span of a single lifetime they have seen the whole face of the earth transformed by the phenomenon of technology. A jet flight over almost any part of the earth today provides striking evidence of this transformation. The fields and highways, factories and cities of man stretch endlessly in every direction. The great primeval forests are rapidly shrinking, and by the end of this century will have essentially disappeared. This is true not only of the developed portions of the globe—Japan, America, Europe, and Russia—but also of those areas we consider underdeveloped—Asia, Africa, and Latin America. Even where the people continue to be economically depressed, technology in the form of steel mills and factories, highways and airports, dams, power plants, and machinery is everywhere in evidence. In this century man has not only filled the whole planet but he has subdued it as well and has taken effective dominion over every creature.

In recent years wilderness and wildlife societies have been formed with a sense of panic about them. Even in Africa, which we still think of as a continent teeming with wild and exotic animals in a natural state, the true situation is one of the rapidly approaching extinction of many species. By the end of this century the only wild animals left on the earth will be found in zoos or scattered national parks maintained by man for their protection. All the rest of the planet will be devoted directly to man and his needs: to the production of his food and of the water and energy to do his work; to his vast cities and the system of highways, air lanes, and seaways linking them together; to his recreation and pleasures, foibles, fancies, and vanities. Occasionally he will visit a zoo or a wildlife preserve and sense the pathos of a vanished world before man took his God-given dominion over it, and feel a sharp nostalgia for the earth as it was before man filled it and subdued it. Over all the rest of the earth every square inch of arable land will be devoted to human agriculture in which all that grows and moves will be specially selected crossbreeds far removed from the wild varieties which covered the earth before man began to exercise his dominion. All that lives will be specially suited to the needs of man; any creature which fails to meet his standard will be bred out of existence. This vast change in the status of living things on this planet is the work of but a single century in the whole 4,600-million-year history of the earth.

Now that astronauts completely circle the earth in less than two hours, particularly since the Apollo pictures, we no longer think of the earth as an unlimited, vast, and unending frontier. Almost universally we have come instead to think of it as a relatively small, circumscribed, single ball floating out in the vastness of space. We are conscious of crowding together on this ball. We have begun to worry about the extent to which we have been polluting it and exhausting its precious and limited resources. We have indeed just begun to think of it in the same way that a crew would think of their spaceship.

It is instructive to pursue the analogy of the earth with a large spaceship. An interesting exercise is to write down the design criteria for a large spaceship to carry a crew of some 250 on a forty-year journey through space. Such criteria would include adequate radiation shielding; energy or fuel reserves required for instrument operation, navigation, and heating; assured supplies of air, water, and food for the crew throughout the journey; waste reprocessing and disposal; and many others which can be thought of. Having done this, it is then instructive to ask for each of these design criteria the extent to which the earth, considered as a spaceship, fulfills them. One discovers in carrying out this exercise that the earth is amazingly well designed as a spaceship for carrying a crew of some two to three billion human beings, but not much more, on a long voyage.

It would not be possible to design a more effective and efficient radiation shield for a spaceship than the earth's atmosphere. Although transparent to light, it cuts out completely all the far ultraviolet, X-rays, and higher energy radiations of outer space. The aurora borealis magnificently displays this shield in operation as it prevents all the high-energy electrons and protons which bombard the earth from penetrating closer than sixty miles above its surface. Under this efficient shield the only radiation hazard to which we are exposed is sunburn from the near ultraviolet which does get through.

Let us now consider in greater detail some of the other fundamental requirements for a satisfactory spaceship. First, it must have an adequate source of energy which will last throughout the trip. Next, it must have an adequate food supply or means of producing food for the crew. The air and water reserves in the ship must be kept pure and adequate for all needs. Wastes must be reprocessed or disposed of in ways which will not contaminate the ship. Finally, the crew must not be allowed to increase in numbers, and it must remain unified throughout the journey. Divisions into warring rival subcrews or interpersonal conflicts between crew members would be catastrophic in a spaceship on an extended voyage.

All these elements of a spaceship economy face us in a particularly acute form as we move into the last third of this century. Consider first the basic requirments for energy and water. These are interrelated, and the key to both is nuclear energy. As we consider the vast requirements which face us in the immediate future, it seems remarkably providential that man should have stumbled on nuclear energy and the possibility of its controlled utilization less than thirty years ago. Spurred by the terrible threat of Hitler's Nazi Germany, it was first developed destructively. Yet its discovery has come barely in time to make our continued occupancy of our spaceship possible.

Until only a dozen years ago, man was exclusively dependent on chemical energy (with the minor exception of hydroelectric power) derived from the burning of fossilized fuels, such as coal, oil, and natural gas, with the oxygen of the atmosphere. This form of energy is exceedingly rare, even esoteric, in the universe as a whole. There are very few spots other than the earth in the entire universe where the necessary ingredients for such energy can be found. Nuclear energy, on the other hand, is extremely common and universally present throughout the universe. Our sun is a natural hydrogen bomb in process of continuous explosion, as are the other so-called "main sequence" stars. Our galaxy, the Milky Way, contains some hundred billion such stars, and all the other galaxies are equally thickly populated with them. Most of the matter in the universe is in this form. It is a sobering thought that God has made more hydrogen bombs than he has anything else. There is nothing more common or more natural and universal in all creation. In the fullness of time it was inevitable that man, in the fulfillment of the promise made at his creation, would come to exercise dominion over this universal element of nature as well.

The true role of nuclear energy for man becomes abundantly clear when we consider the post-revolutionary status of man on this planet in the twenty-first century. The earth will then support a total population in excess of seven billion human beings, and we are forced to contemplate a radically different world than the one we knew before the revolutionary changes of this century began. To support such a population in a continuous and stable way will require an immense consumption of energy on a scale far greater than any we have seen so far. It will also require vast quantities of fresh water mainly for irrigation of great desert areas of the earth not previously required for agriculture. Both the requirements for energy and for water can be met only with nuclear energy. We have already reached the danger point with water, and it is inevitable that we shall soon see more and more large nuclear-powered desalinization plants constructed along the coastal deserts all over the earth. Whether we burn the rocks (by extracting uranium for nuclear fission reactors) or burn the sea (by extracting deuterium for thermonuclear power plants), adequate reservers of nuclear fuels are available in the earth for many millennia. By the twenty-first century essentially all the oil in the earth's crust will have been consumed. Coal will be carefully husbanded and converted to liquid fuel for small mobile power systems, such as automobiles and airplanes. To provide electricity, desalted water, and space heating, nuclear power will be universally used. There is no other long-term alternative.

Nothing we will do in nuclear desalinization of the sea will compare, however, with the evaporative power of that natural nuclear power plant, the sun. The action of the sun generates a known supply of fresh water over the land areas of the earth of 72,000 billion gallons of fresh water per day. If all of this supply could be used for man's purposes, it would be twenty times the requirement of a world population of six billion people. It is, however, very poorly distributed for human purposes, so that the limited fertile areas of the earth's land surface receive more than they need and much larger areas are left as arid deserts. An east-west continental divide running from Labrador through southern Canada to Alaska diverts a great deal of water on this continent into the Arctic Ocean through such mighty rivers as the Mackenzie and the Yukon, or into the Hudson Bay through other river systems. A similar divide on the Eurasian continent diverts great quantities of water in Siberia to the Arctic through the Ob, the Yenisei, and the Lena rivers.

Several large-scale engineering projects either under way or planned are designed to capture such wasted water and divert it to arid regions for agricultural purposes. In Australia the Snowy Mountains form a barrier to damp air coming in from the Pacific. A project well advanced there diverts three rivers, which had been carrying water uselessly back into the sea, through mountain tunnels into canyon reservoirs on the other side. From there the water will generate two and a half million kilowatts as it is lowered to irrigate large areas of the arid interior. In this country the diversion of water from the Colorado through the 200-mile Los Angeles Aqueduct, and the more recent 100-mile Colorado River Aqueduct, not only supplies the city of Los Angeles but irrigates the Imperial Valley and land in Mexico as well. The Feather River project in northern California will in time bring much more water to the dry south.

An even more ambitious plan now being given serious study would bring water from the huge Columbia River to several of the dry Western states to the south. The most ambitious project of all is the proposed North American Water and Power Alliance (NAWAPA). In the East this would divert rivers now flowing into James Bay in Canada through a navigable canal into the Great Lakes, raising their level and materially increasing the power from Niagara Falls. In the West a series of dams, lifts, tunnels, and canals would turn water from the Tanana and Copper rivers in Alaska and the Peace in Canada into a hugh artificial lake 500 miles long in the Rocky Mountain Trench west of the Continental Divide, extending from Alaska through British Columbia into Montana. From this lake, much of the states of Utah, Nevada, Arizona, and New Mexico could be irrigated, with water left over for Mexico. A similar project in Russia would divert a portion of the flow of the Ob and Yenisei rivers into an immense lake on the Ob the size of Italy from which the central Soviet steppes would be irrigated.

The planetary scope of these projects gives emphasis to the spaceship character which the technology of the future will more and more take on. The water and air systems of the earth recognize no national boundaries. They belong to the planet as a whole and must be thought of as the common responsibility of all mankind.

The need for water is closely tied in with the need for food. We are already running dangerously short of food for the world's explosively increasing population. The vast surpluses of grain and other staples, which plagued our agricultural system in this country for so many years, are now gone. We will never see them again. Instead, restrictions on land under cultivation will be rapidly removed in the next few years, and the United States and Canada will be shipping greatly increased tonnages of grain and other foods to India, Pakistan, and China, and perhaps for several years to Russia as well. At the same time, extensive increases in world fertilizer production, which are already under way, will be accelerated, and the productivity of land in these countries already under cultivation will be greatly increased.

Food requirements of the developing countries are rising geometrically with the population growth. Even on the most optimistic projection of population growth, India will require in 1985 an additional production of food calories equal to 88 percent of its total consumption in 1965, Pakistan 118 percent, and Brazil 92 percent. For food protein, the additional requirements in 1985 will be 93 percent in India, 121 percent in Pakistan, and 98 percent in Brazil of 1965 consumption. Surplus production in the United States, Canada, Australia, and Argentina cannot possibly meet such demands as this. In 1965 our excess grain production over and above domestic needs and international sales was twenty-three million metric tons. By 1985 we might, with a major effort, increase this to seventy-five million tons, although with real danger of depleting our precious soil resources. Probably we should not go beyond a surplus production of sixty million tons.

The magnitude of the problem we face can be seen in the following artificial example. Suppose we were to try to meet world food needs by bringing new desert lands under cultivation through irrigation. It requires about half an acre of land to produce enough food for the minimum requirements of one person. Since we are now adding a net increase of seventy million human beings *each year* to the world population, we would have to add thirty-five million acres of new land throughout the world each year for the rest of this century to keep up with food needs. This land would have to be supplied with a minimum of thirty billion gallons of irrigation water per day. This is a staggering requirement even for a sophisticated technology.

Many reactions to the world food crisis tend to be overly optimistic about the rapidity with which food production can be expanded. All mankind is profoundly in the debt of the

Rockefeller Foundation and more recently the Ford Foundation for their foresight in recognizing, far in advance of most, the severity of the problem. For twenty-five years now the Rockefeller Foundation has been supporting programs of development of hybrid varieties suitable for tropical agriculture. A high-yield, resistant wheat developed in Mexico has resulted in a seven-fold increase of wheat production in that country between 1945 and 1965, changing it from an importer to an exporter. This wheat has proved well suited to Pakistan and India, and is showing spectacular results there. The development of a new high-yield, resistant, and low-water-requirement dwarf rice at the Rockefeller-Ford International Rice Institute in the Philippines will be a great boon to Southeast Asia and Africa in the years ahead. A hybrid corn developed in Guatemala has been spectacularly successful in Thailand, where in eight years, starting from a practically nonexistent crop, that nation became by 1963 the fourth largest exporter of corn in the world. In all these cases, however, from ten to twenty years were required to develop these new varieties and bring them up to sufficient production for seed. Little else has been done in research and development for tropical agriculture. Doubtless great strides can be made in the next twenty to thirty years in such development, but the time scale cannot be compressed much below such a period. For the remainder of this century the tropical regions of Asia, Africa, and Central and South America will be continually on the ragged edge between staggering annual increases in food production and catastrophic famine. It is not a pleasant outlook.

Another spaceship requirement which is becoming crucial, particularly in the United States, is the necessity for adequate reprocessing and disposal of all wastes. Since the industrial revolution we have been operating at an ever-

tween six and ten billion human beings. When this has been done, the requirements of that population for energy, fresh water, food, and pure air can and will be met, although most of the intellectual energy and scientific and technological skill of humanity will be absorbed by this task.

The projections of population to the year 2000 given earlier are taken from a report of the President's Science Advisory Committee[1] issued in May, 1967. They are called the "high series" in this report because they are based on the assumption that the 1965 levels of age specific human fertility (the probability that a woman of a given age will bear a child) will continue unchanged for the remainder of the century. The report also includes a "low series" based on the assumption that massive world-wide programs of birth control will achieve a 30 percent reduction in human fertility throughout the world in the twenty-year period from 1965 to 1985. Some insight into the magnitude of the problem we face in stabilizing the population can be gained by noting the effect of such an achievement on total population figures. In this low series, world population will reach 4 billion in 1976 rather than 1975, 5 billion in 1989 rather than 1985, and in the year 2000 it will be 6 billion rather than the 7.2 billion of the high series. Birth-control measures do not have appreciable immediate effects on the total population, but in the long range they will affect it substantially. Apart from some massive catastrophe of famine, plague, or nuclear holocaust, the population at the end of the century will almost certainly exceed 6 billion.

The last, and certainly the most difficult, problem in achieving a satisfactory occupancy of our spaceship is the requirement of unity in the crew. It is to this aspect of the problem that Barbara Ward's book, *Spaceship Earth,* [2] on this same general topic, is devoted. When we consider the vast social and political problems which presently confront mankind, the ultimate unification of man on the planet, which must somehow be achieved seems almost unattainable. There are radical conflicts in ideology dividing the world into two vast armed camps. As we crowd closer together on the earth the way must, and I feel confident will, be found for holding these ideologies in some kind of creative balance. Other tensions arising out of deep historic hurts maintain local conflicts in the Middle East, Southeast Asia, among African tribes, and elsewhere on the earth. America and South Africa are powder kegs of racial tension between white and black. Doubtless the achievement of what Barbara Ward calls a "balance of ideology" will involve paroxysms along the way of an intensity greater than any we have so far known. Each will, I believe, bring us closer to that unity which our spaceship status requires. Each of these adjustments will involve, as Miss Ward so fully describes, a move toward a "Balance of Power" and a "Balance of Wealth" in addition to the balance of ideology. All represent drastic changes in the world of warring nation states, of haves and have-nots, which we know now. Yet her searching analysis of all these problems does lead to a kind of guarded optimism about the ultimate outcome.

In order to get any reasonable notion of the magnitude of the challenge which the twentieth century represents in the whole history of our spaceship, it is necessary to consider it from the perspective of the tremendous evolutionary investment which has been made in the earth and her creatures in bringing us to this present turning point. Our sun and its planets were formed together in the same process about four and a half billion years ago. At first all of the planets had dense atmospheres of hydrogen, ammonia, and methane gases. The massive planets like Jupiter and Saturn still retain this atmosphere. The smaller ones slowly lost it at differing rates through the escape of hydrogen from their weaker gravitational fields. Before doing so, however, the ingredients for life were produced on all of them through the action of ultraviolet light from the sun and of lightning flashes in this primordial atmosphere. At the same time, water and carbon dioxide were released out of the solid crusts of the planets by volcanic activity, which was much more intense then than now.

In the first two billion years of her history, the earth acquired in this way her great oceans, which, as they grew, contained in solution amino acids, purines, pyrimidines, and simple sugars washed out of the early atmosphere by frequent rains. By three billion years ago these constituents had become assembled into the first primitive life forms. By two billion years ago a variety of single-celled organisms resembling modern algae had evolved in the oceans. For the first four billion years of the earth's history all life was confined beneath the surface of the oceans in order to be protected from the fierce ultraviolet radiation from the sun in which the earth was bathed in a dwindling atmosphere reduced mainly to nitrogen gas with growing amounts of free oxygen released from carbon dioxide by photosynthesis in the teeming life in the sea.

In the meantime, Mars, being much smaller and lighter than the earth, lost this original atmosphere much more rapidly. Perhaps for a while, a billion or so years, it, too, had thin oceans and a preliminary development of life within them. But even they in time evaporated and escaped. For the past two billion years or so, Mars has been dry and desolate like the moon and without an appreciable atmosphere of any kind. Closer to the sun, Venus, which is nearest in size to the earth, may for a while have been cool enough to have some water as liquid, but not long enough, if at all, for an appreciable amount of carbon dioxide to be converted to solid carbonates as with the earth. Eventually it lost essentially all of its water from the photodissociation of the vapor at high levels and ended up with a thick atmosphere of mostly carbon dioxide with about the same amount of nitrogen in it as the earth's. It is a dense, crushing atmosphere, producing a pressure at the surface sixty to ninety times greater than that on the earth. Under this heat-trap blanket the surface temperature is 800° F or more, hot enough to melt lead. There is nothing at all romantic about Venus, Mars, or the Moon when seen up close as they really are.

People talk very lightly these days about the prevalence of planets like this earth which could support life over a span of billions of years. When they do so they inadvertently trap themselves, it seems to me, into a set of attitudes which prevents their appreciating the earth. There are doubtless many stars with planetary systems in our galaxy. But it must be equally true that the vast majority of planets end up like Mars or Venus or Jupiter. We do not know all the conditions a planet must satisfy to permit the retention of oceans of liquid water for billions of years while allowing the escape of the primordial atmosphere of ammonia and methane in time for a nitrogen-oxygen atmosphere to replace it so that a full and luxurious development of life can take place on it. But these conditions must be very stringent indeed. I myself doubt that there is another place like the earth within a thousand light years of us. If so, the earth with its vistas of breathtaking beauty, its azure seas, beaches, mighty mountains, and soft blanket of forest and steppe is a veritable wonderland in the universe. It is a gem of rare and magic beauty hung in a trackless space filled with lethal radiations and accompanied in its journey by sister planets which are either viciously hot or dreadfully cold, arid and lifeless chunks of raw rock. Earth is choice, precious, and sacred beyond all comparison or measure. The Apollo 8 crew felt this very acutely as they compared the gray desolation of the moon with the distant sparkling white and azure ball in space which they had so recently left.

For most of its history the earth had no concentrated bodies of rich ores. Slowly, over billions of years, two processes working alternately produced them. One is the steady accumulation of radioactive heat deep in the earth's crust, erupting from time to time in great mountain-forming upheavals with volcanoes and earthquakes. In between these geological revolutions, wind and water worked a slow erosion back to flat plains and swamps. Throughout these changes, alternating and selective solution and precipitation, melting and recrystalization, concentrated one compound here and another there in the earth's crust. It is necessary to know that the rich bodies of copper and tin, or iron and uranium, of gold and silver, which we so recklessly gouge out of the earth, took a billion or more years to be concentrated and stocked for our use. They were surely not meant to be squandered in a single century. Yet by the end of the century it seems likely that all of the high-grade deposits of copper, tin, zinc, uranium, and even iron will already have been exhausted. From then on these metals must be extracted at considerably greater cost from less concentrated lower grade ores. Men will look back on the twentieth century as the age in which their spaceship was recklessly raped and her precious stores, accumulated over billions of years, were wastefully and thoughtlessly squandered.

The earth was already four billion years old when a major turning point in her long history took place. An appreciable amount of oxygen had accumulated in the atmosphere which by then had already become much as it is today. From this oxygen an ozone layer was formed in the upper atmosphere which effectively shielded out the ultraviolet radiation from the sun. Following a period of geological upheaval about 600 million years ago, the earth entered a long placid epoch in her history called the Cambrian. During it, under the new freedom from lethal radiation, a vast elaboration of multicellular organisms took place which produced great coral reefs, a profusion of sea animals called "trilobites," and the first fish. In another 300 million years the land had become clothed with vegetation and many insects had evolved. But at that time, when the earth was already 4,300 million years old, there was not a particle of coal, a drop of oil, or a bubble of gas anywhere in her crust. These great reserves of fossil fuels were laid down over the next hundred million years as though the earth were being stocked with them for some future need. Surely this rare and precious resource was also not meant to be recklessly squandered in a single century. Yet by the end of this century all of the petroleum and natural gas will have been removed from the earth's crust and burned. The coal will last a few centuries more and will be mainly converted into liquid fuel at considerable cost.

This period of fossil-fuel formation was followed, beginning 200 million years ago, by the age of the great dinosaurs and then, beginning seventy million years ago, by the age of the mammals. When that age ended, just two million years ago, the scene had become very familiar. As yet there were no men in the earth, but otherwise all across Europe and Asia, the Americas, and Africa there were dense forests and fertile steppes clothing the earth in a blanket of green. Throughout this lush verdure were myriads of antelopes and zebras, cattle, horses, and buffalo in herds, deer, tigers, wolves, and badgers all similar to those today. A remarkable planet, a tiny island in the midst of vast reaches of an alien space, had brought forth a magic garden, a teeming wonderland, maintained by a fragile balance of light and heat and gravity. A being like an angel or a demon exploring our portion of the galaxy would react with stunned amazement and delight on reaching such a spot in space, so unlike the myriad other planets he had visited.

Two million years ago, which is practically the present in a 4,600-million-year history, a new geologic epoch called the Pleistocene began. Although it was not evident then, it is now clear that this was the most fateful and decisive moment in the whole long history of the earth. The reason is that the mysterious creative drive in the evolutionary process began then to produce man. The process unfolded in several stages and did not reach our species, *Homo sapiens,* until just some 40,000 years ago. Even then his presence did little to alter the pastoral tranquillity of the earth until quite recently. It was only 10,000 years ago that man first began to practice agriculture and build permanent villages, and only 5,000 years since the first civilizations emerged. But from the moment of his creation the potential was there for a drastic change. This strange new creature would in time fill the earth and subdue it and take dominion over all creatures.

Teilhard de Chardin has emphasized the cosmic scope of the revolution in the earth's history which began with the introduction of man among the manifold species which she had produced by representing it as the transformation of the biosphere into the "noosphere." This word he derives from the Greek "nous" for mind in the same way that the former is derived from the Greek "bios" for life. As Teilhard sees it, when man appeared on the planet it began to be clothed in a sphere of mind and spirit, just as 600 million years earlier, in the other great revolution, the earth at the beginning of the Cambrian began to be clothed with its biosphere. By now the whole planet glows with the phosphorescence of thought and spirit which constitutes the full development of its noosphere some 40,000 years after this strange new species *Homo sapiens* appeared on the planet. Clearly this was a fateful moment for the earth in her immensely long history. The transformation of the biosphere into the noosphere has the potential of becoming a great blessing, carrying the planet to new heights of beauty, loveliness, creativity, and spirituality. It has equally the potentiality of becoming a great curse for the earth, leading finally to the poisoning and fouling of her atmosphere, the choking to death of her rivers and lakes, the transformation of the wild beauty of her wildernesses into vast dump heaps of refuse, the extinction of most species of living things other than man. Which it is to be, a blessing or a curse, is the central question before man in the last third of the twentieth century.

The anthropologist Loren Eiseley fears that it is all too likely to prove to be a curse. In his book, *The Firmament of Time,* he looks back on the point at which *Homo sapiens* first appeared as a turning point of dark foreboding for the earth in her beauty. With the first emergence of man, a small dark menacing cloud appeared on the horizon of time. A black hole opened in nature. A dreadful black whirlpool appeared which has been growing and turning faster and faster ever since. In his words:

> It is with the coming of man that a vast hole seems to open in nature, a vast black whirlpool spinning faster and faster, consuming flesh, stones, soil, minerals, sucking down the lightning, wrenching power from the atom, until the ancient sounds of nature are drowned in the cacophony of something which is no longer nature, something instead which is loose and knocking at the world's heart, something demonic and no longer planned—escaped, it may be—spewed out of nature, contending in a final giant's game against its master.[3]

By the end of this century the earth will be really *full* of men. But, worse, it will have already been subdued and despoiled by man. All over its surface his sprawling cities will pollute the landscape. Without limit in every direction the fields and factories of man, his highways and bridges and power lines, will cover the earth. All of the rich accumulations of iron, copper, tin, and many other metals will have been gouged out of the earth and squandered. The total supply of oil and gas, so painstakingly accumulated and stored in the earth for man 200 million years ago, will already have been drawn out and burned. Most of the strange and lovely species of animals and birds with which man so recently shared the adventure of life will have become extinct. A few will remain in national parks and zoos maintained by man in his nostalgia for a lost paradise. The great rivers and lakes of the earth will all have been fouled and dead or dying, and the atmosphere above will reek with the vast outpouring of offal from the cities and factories of man.

Everything about the contemporary scene supports Loren Eiseley's gloomy view of the path to catastrophe along which mankind is headed. Should it continue this way, it can only prove to have been a cosmic blunder to have ever allowed man to evolve on the earth. Never before in the long, amazing, and wonderful history of the course of life on this planet had the introduction of a single species proved to be a lethal factor for all other species and indeed for the ecological principle on which the earth up to then had depended for the support of the whole process of life. In the remainder of this chapter I wish to discuss this self-defeating and destructive aspect of the noosphere in terms of four essential elements. These are the thrust of science and technology, the exercise of dominion, the theological dimension of the earth, and the future of man.

Throughout this century public support and enthusiasm for science and technology have been on a steady course of ascendancy. This has been particularly true since the end of World War II, or, broadly speaking, during the middle third of the century. Science has become the primary status symbol and the object of unquestioning worship throughout the world in every nation and culture. The central dogma of this era has been that science is a great boon to mankind. Programs to stimulate the motivation of our young people toward careers in science have concentrated on the glories of its past achievements and its unlimited capacity to benefit mankind. Hearings before Congressional committees for the appropriation of public funds to support science have brought out many dramatic examples of the way in which science has benefited mankind. Just recently, however, a change in mood, ominous to the scientific community, has begun to show itself, particularly in the United States, Canada, and the United Kingdom. Under heavy budget pressures, congresses and parliaments and the public at large have begun to question this dogma of the benefits of science. In the United States vast sums in the neighborhood of 100 billion dollars have been invested in it since the early 1940's. What does the public have to show for this tremendous outpouring of its treasure?

Similar questions are beginning to be raised within the scientific community itself. At their first discovery, DDT and phosphate-based detergents were hailed as tremendously beneficial contributions of science to humanity. But now that both are being produced and consumed in volumes measured in many millions of tons we are not so sure. Rachel Carson's *Silent Spring* and the dreadful ecological affront to our great lakes and rivers in America resulting from a massive utilization of these "boons to humanity" have given us all second thoughts.

The eminent microbiologist René Dubos works and lives in Manhattan as a professor in the Rockefeller University. The environment in which he is continually immersed strikes him as simply absurd from the standpoint of any rational assessment of the human potential for benefiting mankind. In his recent book[4], he analyzes the varied environments necessary for the full development of a human person in the light of man's deepest evolutionary needs. Out of this analysis he questions profoundly whether science as presently practiced is not really doing mankind more harm than good. Elsewhere in a paper he prepared for the UNESCO conference of 1968 on man and the biosphere, he says:

> Everywhere, societies seem willing to accept ugliness for the sake of increase in economic wealth. Whether natural or humanized, the landscape retains its beauty only in the areas that do not prove valuable for industrial and economic exploitation. The change from wilderness to dump heap symbolizes at present the course of technological civilization. Yet the material wealth we are creating will not be worth having if its creation entails the raping of nature and the destruction of environmental charm.

There is something very wrong in the exercise of man's dominion over the earth if the ultimate effect of his much-vaunted technology is to convert the wilderness to a dump heap. We require a massive redirection of our science and technology if we are to avoid disaster. The course of science has been marked by ever-increasing fragmentation into narrower and narrower specialties. Our best scientists concentrate their genius on understanding increasingly tiny segments of nature without concern for the over-all network of relationships by which nature as a whole hangs together. Any student interested in developing skills in this latter aspect of science will experience great difficulty in finding any department or professor willing to sponsor him. Applications of science which emerge out of this compartmentalized system are made by scientists equally insensitive to the balance of nature whose concerns and understanding are primarily centered on their own particular specialties.

Man is as much a part of nature as stones, and trees, and other mammals. In the exercise of his dominion over the rest of nature he cannot lift himself out of nature. Man and his planet are inextricably bound together. When he inadvertently applies his scientific skills in ways that upset the balance of nature, man is as much a victim of the imbalance as the rest of nature because he is as much a component of nature as everything else. Yet the whole delicate fabric of interrelationships and laws which determine the balance of nature are as much an object for scientific investigation and understanding as any of the multiplicity of prestigious narrow specialties which now consume our best scientific talent. If science is not ultimately to destroy itself, a way must be found to divert increasing numbers of our most talented students into these broader concerns. It is distressing that so many in the scientific community regard ecology and similar broad fields of science with disdain and even contempt. They are blind to the self-destructiveness of their own attitudes and unable to perceive the disaster to which the very narrowness of their own interests and concerns is leading us all.

The existence of the noosphere is evidence of the inescapable role which man alone among all the innumerable species of living things must play in the exercise of dominion over the rest of nature. There is no way for him to escape this role. Yet throughout the course of Western civilization he has used his dominion over nature with arrogance and contempt for everything but himself. Nature has been an enemy to be conquered and enslaved. This has been particularly true of our past performance here in America. The great heroes of our American past are those who pitted great energy and skill against nature. The country was wild and hostile. The honor and glory of man lay in his will and determination to conquer and subdue an enemy of such overwhelming power and magnitude. This tradition of nature as the dark and fearful adversary lies deep in our cultural roots. It permeates the ancient literatures of Greece and Rome. It is enshrined in the legends of Norsemen, the Germanic tribes, and in Beowulf. All the evidence which archaeologists have been able to unearth from the primitive pre-history of mankind indicates that this attitude toward nature is deeply ingrained in the earliest experience of our species. Only in the twentieth century, with the full development of our science and technology and the conversion of the earth into our spaceship, are we beginning to stand aghast at the consequences of this attitude toward nature.

A number of years ago I had the privilege of reviewing a book, *Tomorrow Is Already Here,* by the Swiss journalist Robert Jungk. The book was not well received, and it is my impression that it did not do very well. Several people took vigorous exception to it and to my review. No doubt the picture it presented of America was overdrawn and one-sided, as these objectors claimed. But I was convinced then and am even more persuaded now that there was a disturbingly valid element of truth in that picture. The book has stayed with me, hauntingly, ever since. One quotation from the introduction will give an idea of its contents and purpose:

> America is striving to win power over the sum total of things, complete and absolute mastery of nature in all its aspects. This bid for power is not directed against any nation, class or race. . . . The stake is higher than dictators' seats and presidential chairs. The stake is the throne of God. To occupy God's place, to repeat his deeds, to recreate and organize a man-made cosmos according to man-made laws of reason, foresight and efficiency: that is America's ultimate objective. Toward this her chief efforts are directed.
>
> This is a revolution as convinced of its successful outcome as any other revolutionary movement. . . . It destroys whatever is primitive, whatever grows in disordered profusion or evolves through patient mutation. What it cannot observe and measure, it subdues indirectly to its power. It says the unsayable. It knows no awe.[5]

It is this absence of awe, of any sense of the sacredness of nature, that is terrifying. It is this that drives the whirlpool. Loren Eiseley tells of a conversation he had with a young man who, as a solution to overpopulation, wanted eventually to kill off everything else so that we could live here by ourselves on synthetic food and with more room. Commenting on the colossal insensitivity of this new asphalt animal, Eiseley says of him: "For him there was no eternal, nature did not exist save as something to be crushed, and that second order of stability, the cultural world, was, for him, also ceasing to exist."[6] It is an appalling thought to conceive a future world made up of such men.

There is no suggestion here of a return to nature-in-the-raw, to the wilderness untouched by man. This is clearly impossible in a world twice as crowded as it is now. Moreover, there is simply no way in which man can avoid or escape from his God-given dominion over the rest of nature. Even before man, life at all previous stages in its development has always profoundly affected the environment and structure of the planet. Ancient fossils in the rocks of mountain peaks, the great chalk cliffs of Dover, and the great coal beds in the earth's crust all bear witness to this fact of planetary history. Man represents a new level in this ancient power of life to transform the planet. The conversion of the biosphere into the noosphere is the decisive dominion which once exercised can never again be relinquished.

There are, however, alternative ways in which man can exercise his dominion over the earth. Such an alternative is suggested by René Dubos[7] in the book to which we have already referred. He quotes the Hindu, Tagore, who recalls a journey across Europe by rail in his youth during which he "watched with keen delight and wonder that continent flowing with richness under the age-long attention of her chivalrous lover, Western humanity." This exercise of dominion in love he refers to as an active wooing of the earth. Indeed, as one travels over England even today one is impressed with the potential of this kind of dominion for achieving a new level of beauty and perfection in the earth never before known in her pre-human history. English gardens and parks, the neat and lush countryside, the instinctive grace of groupings of lovely buildings in towns and villages so well adapted to the wider area they serve; all this bespeaks a relationship of man and the earth which enriches and ennobles both. The same impression is created by a field of hybrid corn in Iowa, or a green pasture with a herd of finely bred cattle, or the area of Washington, D. C., between the Capitol and the Lincoln Memorial and the drive along the Potomac there.

Many of the ruins of Roman civilization bear witness to similar relation between man and nature. Wellard James describes the ghost city of Leptis Magna, which in its day was a monument to the genius of Roman engineering skill with irrigation and agriculture in making of the desert a vast producer of grain and olive oil for the empire. Even today, he writes, "As the visitor walks down the Via Triomphale and through the arch of Septimius, he has the feeling that he is in a city not of a dead civilization . . . the warehouses line the quays, the customhouse is open for business, great markets are strategically placed . . . the vast buildings sparkle with life, and the long streets with their latticed fountains and marble benches lead the visitor enchanted to the sea through a series of triumphal arches."[8]

This exercise of dominion in love, this active wooing of the earth, could, if universally practiced with all the resources of modern science and technology, gradually transform our spaceship into an object of grandeur and loveliness of which it could never have been capable without man. For man it would mean the restoration of a life-giving, truly human environment nurturing and elevating his spirit again to new heights of achievement. For the earth it would be the full development of the potentialities of the noosphere and a transformation as great and wonderful as that earlier one in which she acquired the biosphere. But it cannot be achieved without love.

To love the earth in the way required for this kind of exercise of man's dominion over her demands the achievement of a new level of respect and appreciation for her. This in turn requires a reawakened sense of the sacredness and holiness of the earth and her creatures. There must be a reverence for the earth which recoils from the thought of desecration of her atmosphere, her water, and her land as a sacrilege. This in turn requires the development of a whole new theology of nature. Let us turn then to a consideration of the nature and content of such a theology and of the basis on which it might be constructed.

In the twenty-five or so centuries of man's religious history prior to this century, he felt little need to look at nature theologically. Rather, nature was simply there, a given, out of which he might possibly extract a natural theology. He would simply use nature as a means for understanding God. Natural theology starts with nature as given and asks what it has to tell us about God, or what moral guidelines for action can be derived from it through a discovery of the natural law. What I am proposing is a reversal of this approach. I would like to begin with God as a given, as revealed in the historic experience of Israel culminating in His own incarnation in that history, and go from there to nature. Such an approach would produce a true theology of nature. It is just the reverse of natural theology.

A great deal of modern theology is scornful of the "nature religions" against which the "history-rooted religion" of the Bible is arrayed. There is much to be said in defense of the validity of this position. The religion of pre-Israelite Canaan with its Baals and fertility cults involved much that was degrading and corrupting, and, on balance, did more harm than good for the devotees. But all of the primitive nature religions enshrine an element which we desperately need to recover. I do not, of course, suggest a return to dryads and numens, but I would plead for a rediscovery of the sense of the sacredness and holiness of things which they possessed in such a vivid and lively fashion.

There is increasing emphasis, as indeed there must be, on programs of conservation, control of pollution, urban renewal, and environmental health. The concern of all nations with these problems must be greatly intensified in the years ahead. Yet the very words used to describe these programs point to their complete man-centeredness. They are described and conducted solely in the interests of man and his welfare. Yet the earth in all her beauty is our mother. She bore us. When we pour filth into her atmosphere, befoul her lakes and rivers, disfigure her landscape with our junk piles, and wantonly squander her precious resources we desecrate her as well as endanger ourselves and our own interests. The earth has an integrity of her own independent of us. No single species she has produced in her long history has a right to destroy her and her other creatures. We need to develop a healthy and holy fear of doing so.

If man in some super-mad moment should destroy himself in a vast nuclear holocaust, one could perhaps say of it that it would serve him right. The rest of the universe could do without such a creature in the future. Yet such a thought immediately suggests another, for man and his destiny are inextricably linked to the earth. In destroying himself, he must inevitably destroy much of the earth with him. Surely the whole universe would cry out in anguish at such an act. We have seen how rare and choice a gem the earth is in the vast reaches of space. Rarely can the delicate balance of many factors be achieved to permit such a magic wonderland to develop. It is a sacrilege of awful proportions to desecrate and despoil such a place with its long evolutionary investment and immense evolutionary potential. In the realm of reality transcendent to space and time such an act would not be easily forgiven.

Yet the continuation of present trends through just the remaining thirty years of this century will mean just such a desecration. The volume of atmospheric pollutants and the annual accumulation of solid wastes produced by a planetary population double that of the present will be more than doubled. The blight of ugliness and urban sprawl produced by twice as many people in a short thirty years is dreadful to contemplate. The earth so recently graced with vast forests and windswept steppes, with sparkling clear lakes and mighty rivers, will hang denuded, befouled, and despoiled in space. The work of billions of years of slow evolutionary achievement will in a single century have been undone and ruined. Surely somewhere in the heart of the mystery of this strange universe there must be a cry of anguish at such desecration. We have to do here with a sacrilege of such cosmic scope that it is impossible to deal with it in purely secular terms. Only in terms of a fully developed and solidly grounded theology of nature can we hope to cope with it.

For man himself another moral and theological problem presents itself with urgency. As we have seen, in the remaining third of this century man will have fulfilled the Biblical injunction to be fruitful and multiply and fill the earth. An inescapable corollary of this injunction faces us now with terrible urgency. Because the earth is in fact a spaceship for man's journey, it is essential that once the earth has been filled by man he must stop being fruitful and cease further multiplication. Moreover, this must be accomplished within a generation, or certainly within no more than two generations. The children of today's college graduates must, as they approach adulthood, already have started the process which their children must complete; namely, that of separating human sexuality from procreation. All over the world this process will involve a profound religious and moral readjustment. Yet there is no viable alternative to such a transformation. What God required of man during the long centuries before he filled the earth is quite different from what He will require of man after he has done so. This seems clear enough. Once the crew of the spaceship has reached its full complement, there is an absolute requirement that it not be allowed any further increase. Yet no other requirement calls for such a deep-seated readjustment in long-established religious, moral, and social patterns, or is more resolutely resisted by mankind.

There is much in the present predicament of man and his planet which suggests a Greek tragedy. The path ahead unfolds with a terrible inevitability toward a doom which we do not know how to avoid or escape. The great whirlpool has already gained so much momentum and turns so fast that we do not see any way to stop it. In the end, when it has devoured the earth and the rest of nature, will it not at last suck man, too, into its black and bottomless maw?

There is nothing I can point to of what can be foreseen from the present situation which offers any hope of a way out of this awful dilemma. Yet I do have a genuine and confident hope in the ultimate outcome. Necessarily it is a religious hope, since it must count on completely unforeseeable developments. It is grounded in a conviction of meaning and purpose in the long evolutionary process which produced man on this planet and brought him to his present predicament. Too much investment has gone into him to have it wiped out completely. Admittedly it will take a miracle to save man, but my hope is grounded in an expectation of just such a miracle. The past history of our species is marked with many such miracles wholly unforeseen by those involved in them, but constituting major turning points in human development. There is every reason for confidence that this element will continue to mark our future history.

Even with this ultimate hope, however, I do not believe there will be any escape from the agony which awaits us in the immediate future. As we are crowded and compressed together in the next decade or two, there are bound to be social paroxysms of an intensity very much greater than any we have experienced so far. Sooner or later before the end of the century, catastrophic famine, with its attendant threat of epidemic disease and disruption of established order, is highly probable. The last third of the twentieth century will surely be a time of judgment for man of a severity far greater than any our species has ever before experienced. Much that we hold dear and have long cherished will be destroyed, never to be recovered. It is the way of the cross for the whole of mankind on the planet. But beyond the cross is Easter; that is the hope.

For 30,000 years men were exclusively hunters and gatherers for food. Civilization began to dawn sporadically around the world only some 5,000 years ago. Until it came, no one could have conceived of what it would be like to live in organized communities of towns and cities, to build imposing buildings and monuments, to have a written literature, and to forge empires. Perhaps the time of judgment we are entering in the last third of this century is the next such step in human evolution; the twilight zone of civilization and the dawn of a new age. After the death of civilization, something new will rise from its ashes as different from the civilization we have known for the last 5,000 years as that civilization was from the long precivilized experience of man. We have no way to even conceive what post-civilization will be like. In some way a new kind of planetary unity of man should emerge, involving new structures and new vistas. In the retrospect of succeeding centuries it will be seen as a major new step in the cultural evolution of *Homo sapiens.* When it has occurred, it will make the agony of this present age seem worthwhile. Men will then see why that agony was so necessary for the achievement of man's new estate.

In the meantime, we have many vital tasks of immediate urgency facing us. The time of judgment is also a time of challenge and of great opportunity for those with the courage, the faith, and the hope to live confidently in the midst of great revolutionary change, when all that is familiar and secure is crumbling about them. The future of both man and his lovely planet depends on our having such people in this critical time. Through them and their efforts the new age will dawn out of the wreckage of the old. May God raise up many such among us in the decades ahead!

NOTES

1. *The World Food Problem,* A Report of the President's Science Advisory Committee, 3 volumes, Superintendent of Documents, U.S. Government Printing Office.
2. Barbara Ward, *Spaceship Earth,* Columbia University Press: New York, 1966.
3. Loren Eiseley, *The Firmament of Time,* Atheneum: New York, 1962; p. 123.
4. René Dubos, *So Human an Animal,* Scribners: New York, 1968.
5. Robert Jungk, *Tomorrow Is Already Here,* Simon and Schuster: New York, 1954.
6. op. cit. p. 128.
7. op. cit. pp. 194–208.
8. Wellard James, *The Great Sahara,* E. P. Dutton & Company: New York, 1965.

SCARCITY

PEOPLE AND FOOD

by Dr. Ivan Bennett, Jr.

> *. . . . and it shall come to pass that, when they shall be hungry, they shall fret themselves, and curse their King and their God. . . .*
>
> ISAIAH 8:21

> *. . . . and lo a black horse; and he that sat on him had a pair of balances in his hand. And I heard a voice in the midst of the four beasts say, A measure of wheat for a penny, and three measures of barley for a penny; and see thou hurt not the oil and the wine.*
>
> REVELATION 6:5,6

This chapter is concerned with the population explosion and the world food shortage, surely two of the most complex and serious problems that mankind must face in the last third of this century. The discussion will center on the developing countries. Although the problem of overpopulation is not limited to these lands, it is there that it is most severe and already has led to an inadequate amount of food, the situation that adds urgency to finding a solution.

If one examines in depth and detail conditions in the low-income countries of Asia, Africa, and Latin America in terms of food supply, in terms of public health, in terms of education, in terms of housing, in terms of transportation, or in terms of standard economic indicators such as per capita income, level of employment or productivity, one is driven to the inevitable conclusion that the condition of life of the nearly two-thirds of the human race that inhabits those areas is deteriorating. Depending upon one's viewpoint, then, the plight of this "third world" can be expressed euphemistically as overpopulation, as hunger, as disease, as illiteracy, or as chronic poverty. All of these terms are descriptive of different facets of the same problem. Hunger and rapid population growth are not primary diseases of the developing countries. Rather, they are the symptoms of a deeper, underlying malady —*lagging economic development.*

The fundamental core of development might be described as *choice.* The true essence of human freedom is the set of choices that human beings are permitted to make. When their vocational, economic, social, political, educational, and nutritional choices are enlarged, a people's freedom is expanded. Many battles for independence have been fought and won and many new nations have left the ranks of colonialism to join the family of politically independent states. The bright light of a better tomorrow has not yet dawned for most of the citizens of the emerging nations. The newly acquired political freedom has not yet broadened the set of choices available to them. It is in this sense that the problem boils down to one of economic development.

Some figures will help to define the problem and to understand its magnitude:

	Developed Rich Countries	*Developing Poor Countries*
Population	1.0 billion	2.3 billions
Rate of population increase	1.3%	2.5%
Per capita income	$1,800.	$110.
G.N.P. growth rate	3–4%	2.5–4%
Per capita growth, G.N.P.	1.7–2.7%	0–1.5%

In terms of an individual's income, a 4 percent rise in G.N.P. has a very different meaning in these two situations. In the developed country, it adds $50 per year; in the developing country it adds $1 to $2. A person's choices change very little if his earnings rise by only $1 or $2 per year.

My own deep concern with this over-all problem began abruptly in the spring of 1966 when I was appointed chairman of a panel of the President's Science Advisory Committee, charged by President Lyndon B. Johnson to conduct a comprehensive study of the world food problem. Until then my entire professional career had been devoted single-mindedly to the study of medicine. I had some notion, of course, from medical experience overseas, of problems of malnutrition in the developing countries, but I had utterly no conception of the all-encompassing urgency of the food-population problem. I am now convinced that, with the possible exception of the pursuit of peace, it should be the foremost concern of every government on earth.

The World Food Panel eventually recruited more than a hundred knowledgeable and experienced individuals from government, industry, universities, and foundations as the problem of world hunger began to unfold in awesome complexity. The study required nearly a year to complete, and the results were finally published in a three-volume report of more than 1,300 pages.[1] The report concentrates upon the needs and prospects during the two decades between 1965 and 1985, and its four basic conclusions are simply stated:

1. The scale, severity, and duration of the world food problem are so great that a massive, long-range, innovative effort, unprecedented in human history, will be required to master it.

2. The solution of the problem that will exist after 1985 *demands* that programs of population control be initiated now. For the immediate future, the food supply is critical.

3. Food supply is directly related to agricultural develop-

ment and, in turn, agricultural development and over-all economic development are critically interdependent in the hungry countries.

4. A strategy for attacking the world food problem will, of necessity, encompass the entire foreign-assistance effort of the United States in concert with other developed countries, voluntary institutions, and international organizations.

The basic problem of world hunger is that of uneven distribution of the food supply among nations, within countries, and among families with different levels of income. Statistical surveys show that there is no *global* shortage of food, either in terms of quantity (measured in *calories*) or quality (measured as *protein*). There is overwhelming evidence of undernutrition (insufficient calories) and malnutrition (lack of protein or vitamins) in the developing countries, a clear indication that statistical averages do not portray the actual amounts and quality of food consumed by millions of individuals in the world.

Even in countries where the average diets are nutritionally inadequate according to the minimum standards of the United Nations Food and Agriculture Organization (FAO), surveys show that the poorest classes of the population consume diets with caloric and protein contents that are 25 percent *below* the national average and, therefore, fall far below the minimal standards. All over the world, in both developing and developed countries, it is in the low-income segment of the population that overt malnutrition is found, particularly among the most susceptible groups: infants and preschool children, pregnant women, and nursing mothers.

The rich are seldom hungry. No matter where he happens to be in the world, an individual who has enough money can buy all the food that he wants. Hunger and malnutrition are, to a certain extent, the result of ignorance, but, primarily, they are problems of inadequate income. The root problem in Latin

America, Asia, and Africa is lagging income, the result of lagging economic development.

When one's purchasing power is limited, of course, *food* is likely to be the first commodity that is missed, since, in its absence, the pangs of hunger occur within hours. It is not surprising then, that *the price of food is one of the prime economic indicators in the developing countries.*

The experience of Indonesia points up this important role of food. A 1965 survey of low- and middle-income Indonesian families, carried out daily for thirty days in each household, showed that expenditures for food took up between 65 and 70 percent of family income, of which at least two-thirds went for rice, the staple food-grain of the Indonesian diet. (A similar survey in Chile showed 70 to 80 percent of family income spent for food. The comparable figure for American families is about 18 percent of income spent for food.) The price of rice clearly exerts a controlling effect upon the Indonesian family budget and, hence, upon the national economy. It is highly likely that this situation will prevail as long as per capita income remains low and rice continues to be the principal food.

In 1967 the importance of the price of rice in Indonesian economic development was demonstrated dramatically and beyond doubt. Through a serious and austere effort to stabilize its currency, aided by funds from developed nations, the Indonesian Government had reduced the inflation rate from an enormous 650 percent in 1966 to about 50 percent by the fall of 1967. An unexpectedly long dry season reduced the 1967 rice harvest by 20 percent and, in the absence of imported rice to make up the unanticipated deficiency, the price of rice rose sharply, followed by increased prices for other food and then non-food commodities. The inflation rate more than doubled, soaring to 112 percent within two months. The result of this bitter experience was to focus the attention of government economic planners upon the key role of agricultural production, particularly rice production.

The latest five-year development plan, adopted in February of 1969 and known as "Repelita," gives first priority to the development of agriculture, with the goal of making the country an exporter, rather than an importer, of rice. Until now, Indonesia has imported about $100 million worth of rice each year, yet the Indonesian population already is principally engaged in agriculture. More than 70 percent of the people live in rural areas and depend upon farming for a living. "To anyone who watches farmers here bending over their rice fields, or carrying huge loads on their backs from dawn to midafternoon, the oft-heard assertion that Indonesians are indolent is an obvious slander. But they are resistant to change because of their culture and their poverty.... New methods and seeds are slow to be accepted."[2]

The complexities of Indonesia's food problems, illustrative of those in many other developing nations, were summarized by Sultan Hamenku Buwono IX, Minister of State for Economic, Financial, and Industrial Affairs:

> In conclusion allow me to mention the following contradiction. Our soil is fertile, our climate is most favorable to agriculture, and especially for food production, we have millions of hectares of arable land and many more millions of virgin lands, irrigation water sources are waiting for exploitation, our petanis, or farmers, are hard-working people and have accumulated a wealth of experience in many centuries, and yet our people are poor, and food is available for many of us only in scant supply. Why is this so? What are the reasons?[3]

At this point, I would inject a personal note. During the course of the study conducted by the World Food Panel, I discovered that about all that modern agriculture and medicine have in common is that each is an applied biological science. More important, I became keenly aware of differences in the public's image of medicine and of agriculture. Furthermore, because I am convinced that this difference in attitudes epitomizes a prime factor in the apparent inability of the developing nations to solve their food problems and their apparent unwillingness to avail themselves of the assistance which is proffered by the developed nations, I wish to discuss it briefly.

Most Americans look upon the practice of medicine as a highly scientific profession, and would not think of arguing with or second-guessing a physician (unless it concerns his bill) or seek the advice of non-professionals, no matter how highly respected in medical matters. Without arguing this attitude on its merits, I would contrast it with that toward agriculture. Most individuals (and I include myself until recently) assume that they are (or could easily become) knowledgeable in agriculture—because they equate *agriculture* and *farming,* which they believe requires only soil, seeds, perhaps a little fertilizer, and, particularly, plenty of *hard work.* Millions of Americans garden as a form of recreation, and they find it easy to equate what I now call "subsistence horticulture," which is always a money-losing proposition, with *commercial farm production,* which is *not* primarily a recreational pursuit. In most American neighborhoods the finest garden belongs to the man who works hardest in it or who can afford to hire someone to work in it. This immediate perception of farm productivity as being related to physical effort is all too easily transferred to American thinking about the world food problem. Hence, one repeatedly encounters the view that the inability of subsistence farmers in the traditional societies of the developing nations to produce the food that their countrymen need is a sign of either *laziness* or *ignorance.* The substance of modern agricultural science, its possibilities and limitations, and the importance of physical and biological inputs such as fertilizer, pesticides, and good seeds, and of adaptive research, of the market structure, and of transportation, processing, storage, and distribution systems do not enter into popular thinking about the problem, being so taken for granted here in our own country that the existence of this so-called infrastructure is assumed everywhere in the world.

After all, people must eat, and they have been able to eat through the centuries no matter how primitive their economy or how underdeveloped their science, so why don't the farmers overseas just get down to work?

There is also a widespread belief, quite erroneous, that because many of the world's farmers are illiterate, they are stupid and will not respond rationally. Dr. F. F. Hill, a renowned international agricultural consultant, has characterized this attitude as nonsense: "Just because a man can't read is no sign that he can't figure." Dr. Lowell Hardin of the Ford Foundation has said: "Farmers in Latin America repeatedly tell us, 'Give us a market, assure us an adequate price, and we'll produce more.' "[4]

Recently developments here in the United States offer hope that the American public may be coming to understand the realities of the food-population problem. The world problem is epitomized by the "discovery" of hunger and malnutrition in the United States, largely as a result of the investigation of conditions in the Mississippi delta led by Senators Robert Kennedy and Jacob Javits in 1967. Until that time, most politicians had denied that hunger existed, had blamed it on the unwillingness of people to go out and get a job, or simply had called for more welfare money. There is now a Senate committee on hunger, headed by Senator George McGovern. They have found and are telling the nation that hunger in the United

States is no simple problem and that there is no simple solution:

> Until now people have been calling it the "hunger committee." But after their first trip last week in southwest Florida, members of the Senate Select Committee on Nutrition and Human Needs were paying increased attention to the second part of the title.
>
> For they found heart-rending evidence that hunger is inseparable from a whole tangle of human problems.
>
> The search for hunger led to a circular trail of squalid housing, lack of sanitation, bad health, poor education and limited job opportunities:
>
> The senators found that children may receive free breakfasts and lunches and still stay sick because of home conditions. . . .
>
> Some of the senators were openly irritated by local officials who denied that there were any serious problems among the poor, or insisted that they were someone else's concern. . . .
>
> The first traveling hearing suggested . . . that food alone will not crack the cycle of human misery. It may take an assault from all directions.[5]

The budget of the U.S. Department of Agriculture for 1968–69 reveals the policy dilemma clearly. Expenditures for stabilizing farm income were $4.5 billion, while the amount spent to distribute surplus food or to provide "food stamps" to the poor was $560 million. This means that the nation was spending eight times as much to prop up farm prices as to assure that poor citizens receive adequate diets.

The confusion and difficulty surrounding efforts to formulate policies and programs to alleviate hunger among the disadvantaged in America, the most affluent nation in the world, have great meaning for the world-wide situation. If we in the United States cannot remove the political obstacles to allow us to eradicate our comparatively small domestic hunger problem, the much more difficult and complex international problem is a formidable threat indeed.

The growing difference in the levels of living between the developed and the developing countries is largely the result of the technological revolution. This revolution has led to rapid and self-sustaining economic growth and steady elevation of living standards in the developed nations. In the developing countries, until now, however, it has had only one critical important effect, a *striking reduction in death rates.* This reduction in mortality has not been accompanied by a reduction in birth rates.

The result of these unbalanced "benefits" of modern public health has been an unprecedented rate of population growth of many of the poor nations. An inordinately rapid rise in human numbers is perhaps the most significant characteristic of most developing countries. It is one of the basic causes of the widening economic disparity between the two parts of the world.

The times required to double the population in most developing countries are eighteen to twenty-seven years; they are fifty-five to eighty-eight years in most developed nations. The developing regions now contain about two-thirds of the world's human beings. By the year 2000, if present rates of growth continue, there will be four times as many people in the developing countries as in the developed ones.

The World Food Panel of the President's Science Advisory Committee prepared estimates of world population trends during the years from 1965 to 1985 as a basis for calculating world food requirements during that period. Detailed estimates were also made for three countries, India, Pakistan, and Brazil. It is to be emphasized that the data on which such projections are made are always incomplete. According to Dr. Forrest Lindner, only about 67 percent of the world's population is subject to any type of census-taking, and up-to-date information about birth rates and death rates is available for only slightly more than 50 percent.[6]

Some of the assumptions that went into the population projections will be mentioned because they are important to understanding the problem and because, in a small way, they illustrate some of the technical demographic complexities of making population projections.

Two sets of figures were calculated, a *high* series, based on the assumption that fertility would remain at present levels and a *low* series, based on a decline in fertility levels. It was assumed that mortality would decline at the same rate in both series. For the high series it was not assumed that *birth rates* (birth per 1,000 total population) would remain constant, but, rather, that *age-specific fertility,* the probability that a woman of given age will bear a child, would remain constant. Birth rates fluctuate according to the age-sex structure of a population.

For the low series it was assumed that the intensified family-planning programs introduced in 1965 would cause age-specific fertility to decline to 90 percent of the 1965 value by 1970, to 80 percent by 1980, and to 70 percent by 1985.

If fertility does not change, and mortality continues to decline, the population of the world will increase from 3.3 billion in 1965 to 5.0 billion in 1985, or by 52 percent. With a 30 percent decrease in fertility during the two decades, the world population would be 4.65 billion by 1985, an increase of about 40 percent above 1965. The difference between the high and the low figures is only 385 million persons, but would become greater in later years. For example, by the year 2000, the high series would give a world population of 7.15 billion and the low series would give 6.0 billion. These and the figures for Pakistan, India, and Brazil are shown below:

	1985 population in millions	
	low	*high*
World	4,650	5,030
Pakistan	211	241
India	768	864
Brazil	138	150

These figures were then used to estimate the percent increase in calories and in protein that would be required to bring dietary standards of the increasing population up to the minimal requirements of the United Nations Food and Agriculture Organization:

		% increase in 1985 over needs in 1965			
Needs	*Population estimate, 1985*	*World*	*India*	*Pakistan*	*Brazil*
Calories	High	52	108	146	104
	Low	43	88	118	92
Protein	High	52	110	145	109
	Low	45	93	121	98

These figures are of extreme importance in placing the problems of food and population in perspective. They show that food needs in the hungry countries will more than double by 1985 if present rates of population growth continue. Optimistic estimates of success in population control (a 30 percent reduction in fertility) will reduce food needs in India only by 20 percent, in Pakistan 28 percent, and in Brazil by 8 percent. These are significant reductions, but they will not *solve* the food problem, which is not a *future* threat; it is *here* and *now.*

The effects of successful family planning will become more apparent in the years after 1985. The impact of population control will be realized slowly over a period of many years, but there is an immediate and increasing need for food regardless of the ultimate success in programs of population control.

The critical need for food can be illustrated by pointing out that even to feed the people already born in the developing countries will be an enormous problem because of the large proportion of children in their populations. The amount of food required, of course, increases steadily from the time of birth to about nineteen years of age. Nearly half of those living in the developing countries are less than fifteen years old. To maintain the Indian population at its *present level* of nutrition would require 20 percent more food in 1975 than in 1965 *if no new children were added during this ten-year period.* To elevate the diet to the minimal standard of the United Nations Food and Agriculture Organization, a 30 percent increase would be required. In terms of wheat, those caloric increases represent twenty and thirty million metric tons annually in 1975—more than twice the present amount of U.S. food aid shipments to India and about the increase that can be expected from present trends in Indian agricultural production.

At this point, I wish to emphasize that, while the report of the World Food Panel, as is true of most other reports on this subject, contains many neatly drawn graphs and detailed tables which attempt to quantify food needs and population growth, they are merely crude approximations. When many countries of varying size, with different climates, different soils, with populations which are racially, culturally, and economically differentiated are to be evaluated, the attempt to make aggregate projections from incomplete statistical surveys of what has gone before often leads to a wide difference between those projections and the actual course of events. Furthermore, the whole effort suffers from the unreliability factor introduced by what Dr. Karl Brandt, the eminent agricultural economist, calls "postgraduate jugglers." The chief of the French Government's statistical service said in 1948:

> Under the occupation we taught our farmers how to defeat Hitler's military government in its endeavor to drain food from the farms by adjusting crop and animal production reports. It worked, but our farmers and enumerators learned too well and are now postgraduates in juggling statistics. We in the government must be our own intelligence service, protecting the public as well as the farming community from serious misinformation.

Throughout the developing countries of Asia, Africa, and Latin America, reliable figures on how much of a given food commodity has been planted, harvested, stored, or lost to pests and spoilage are still lacking.

The needs that have been projected for calories and protein are for *consumption* and do not take into consideration losses in production, transportation, or storage so that, if anything, the problem has been underestimated in the figures that have been given.

The disproportionate additional need for food in the developing countries cannot be solved by successful programs of family planning alone during the next several years. This mathematically demonstrable fact of demography must not be interpreted to indicate that population control measures are inherently ineffective or in any way secondary in importance to increasing food production. On the contrary, successful family planning is cumulative and makes itself felt in the size of the next generation. It is imperative to institute intensive programs of family planning now if outpacing of food production by population growth is to be avoided as a problem that might continue well into the next century.

That reduction in population growth is essential to achieving a balance between food supply and food need is an obvious, easily understood, and widely appreciated fact.

There is another, more complex, less well-known and crucially important relationship between nutritional needs and family planning. Surveys of the attitudes of married couples in developing countries show that the number of children desired is higher than in the developed nations. Furthermore, the average number of live births per woman in developing countries is 30 percent greater than the number of children desired.

Emphasis on the desire for heirs leads to large families. Only one son may be needed for ritual or economic purposes, but it is common to want *two* sons to insure against death or incapacity of one. Couples must average four children to obtain two sons.

Availability and efficacy of pills, intrauterine devices, and other technical means for birth control are largely irrelevant until couples have secured the desired number of living children.

If we assume that the necessary preconditions for reducing fertility are low infant and child mortality and a public awareness that mortality is low, then we have the apparent paradox that a reduction in childhood mortality will reduce rather than *raise* the rate of population growth.

In the United States about twenty-five out of every 1,000 live-born infants fail to survive to the age of one year, and most deaths are from prematurity or congenital defects. In the poor countries of Asia, Africa, and Latin America, published infant mortality rates range from 100 to 200 per 1,000 live births. Much of the higher death rate is the direct or indirect result of protein-calorie malnutrition.

Protein-calorie deficiency in the form of *kwashiokor* is a great killer. Acute diarrhea can be a dangerous illness for a well-nourished American baby; in the malnourished infants of the developing countries it has an appalling mortality. Common childhood diseases are catastrophic in protein-deficient children. In 1960, for example, the fatality rate from ordinary measles was more than 100 times greater in Chile than in the U.S.

If lowered infant and child mortality is a precondition to acceptance of family planning and if the major underlying cause of childhood deaths is malnutrition, it follows that an increase in both quantity and quality of food is essential to achieving stabilization of population growth.

Viewed in this light, alleviation of the food problem must be accorded the highest priority in planning for the developing nations.

All aspects of economic growth and social development are complicated and made much more difficult by a high birth rate which results in a very high proportion of children in the population and a heavy burden of dependency upon the working adults. Even if over-all economic growth is taking place, rapid population increase minimizes improvement in per capita income and similarly affects per capita food production.

The poverty of the developing nations constrains their educational expenditures and, with the increasing proportion of children, already meager national educational budgets will be spread even thinner.

The United States spends more on education each year than the entire Indian G.N.P.

Today's poorly educated children in the developing countries will eventually be job-seekers. By 1985, at present rates of growth, the age group fifteen to thirty-four years old, in the three countries, India, Pakistan, and Brazil will grow by 180 million persons. This means that jobs must be created for about 100 million persons entering the labor force for the first time. Nearly all of this increase will come from persons *already* born. Consequently, the magnitude of the employment problem between now and 1985 will not be affected by population control programs instituted now. If the capital investment needed to create a new job averages $1,000, then the total cumulative investment needed for these three countries alone by 1985 would be about $100 billion even to maintain the present very low per capita income!

In order to provide for its additional annual population alone, India needs 126,500 schools, 372,500 schoolteachers, 2.3 million houses, and 4.3 million new jobs.

The fertility rate in all human societies falls well below the potential of human fecundity. The restraints on population growth appear to be social and economic rather than, as Malthus first thought, disease and starvation. Birth rates in the industrialized nations began to fall below those of the primarily agricultural nations about a century ago. There was a growing tendency to postpone marriage, to increase celibacy, to resort to abortion, and to practice contraception, in addition to the limitation of population growth by emigration.

In recent years, rapid decreases in fertility levels have occurred in several developed countries in eastern Europe and in Japan. Fertility rates were lowered by 40 percent in Hungary between 1954 and 1962, by 36 percent in Rumania between 1955 and 1962, and by 30 percent in Poland between 1955 and 1964. The decrease in Japan from 1950 to 1965 was 44 percent. Conditions in these countries differed from those in the developing countries. Literacy rates were high, fertility was already being controlled by significant segments of the population, and the people were strongly motivated to limit family size. The lowest achieved family size in the United States occurred in the mid-1930's before the "pill" and the intrauterine device (IUD) and, in France and Switzerland, the change to smaller families occurred in the early years of the last century. It is not, of course, that newer methods of contraception are not major improvements, but it is noteworthy that the socio-economic pressures to restrict family size preceded them in many countries. As Dr. André Hellegers has pointed out, these considerations have given rise to a polarization of views concerning the approach to the problem of limiting population growth:

> For the sake of simplification it might be said that two camps are forming. One camp might be called the Developmentalists, who contend that, where socio-economic development is achieved, desired family-size automatically decreases, and that is the road to solution of the problem. The other camp might be called the Contraceptivists, who feel that since the practice ultimately taking place in the Western suburban bedroom is one of contraception, the acceptance of these standards by the underdeveloped countries will decrease family-size and improve their economic status.

The dilemma that the world faces in coping with the population problem can be stated simply. It has never been shown that an aid program which supplies contraceptives in and of itself leads to contraception in the absence of economic progress. The other aspect of the problem is that a large part of the benefits of economic aid programs is nullified by population expansion. In actual fact, the solution would seem to be the use of *both* approaches so as to be sure that the appropriate techniques of birth control are available in the hope of hastening the demographic transition when socio-economic and cultural factors decrease the desired family size.

There is yet another polarization of views among demographers and population experts. The two camps here might be called the Family Planners and the Population Planners. The

Family Planners hold that reductions in family size must be on a voluntary basis. Their view is illustrated in the following statement by Dr. Karl Brandt:

> However, because the issue concerns the guaranteed freedom of individuals and nationally enforced laws covering the responsible use and protection of such freedom, the worldwide campaign for planned parenthood can succeed in the long run only if it is steered away from crimes against human dignity and decency and the unwitting or deliberate abolition of individual freedom. Government and public authority may legitimately inform the people about contraception and the risks to physical, mental, and psychic well-being of parents and children which the use of specific means may involve. To supply reliable information on the probable economic and social consequences of having many children in one family or children born at shortest intervals is an equally legitimate function of the State.
>
> But the strongest taboo should be invoked against public interference with the right of married couples to decide for themselves whether they want children at all, how many and at what intervals.[8]

The viewpoint of the Population Planners is expressed by Dr. Kingsley Davis:

> Millions of dollars are being spent on the false assumption that population control can be achieved by family-planning programs. . . .
>
> Clearly, undesired population growth is a collective rather than an individual problem. The number of children couples want is not automatically the number that, from a societal point of view, they should have. To make the individual decisions add up to a desirable population trend, a nation must find ways to influence individual decisions in accord with an over-all plan. Otherwise,

> individual planning will simply result in collective non-planning. . . .
>
> Since measures designed to change social conditions—especially with regard to the family, women's role, sex, and reproduction—are politically dangerous, the safer policy is one of furnishing officially approved contraceptive information and materials to married couples who ask for them. Not only does such a program have little if any effect on the population trend, but it fails even to accomplish the avowed aim of giving people free control over reproduction. . . .
>
> Furthermore, with traditional morality sponsoring familism, and with prosperity and group power viewed as functions of population growth, suggestions of effective anti-natalist policies evoke ridicule, outrage, or worse. . . .
>
> It can be argued that overproduction—that is, the bearing of more than four children—is a worse crime than most and should be outlawed. One thinks of the possibility of raising the minimum age of marriage, of imposing stiff penalties for illegitimate pregnancy, of compulsory sterilization after a fifth birth. . . .
>
> The *sine qua non* of a population policy is that people be induced to curb their reproduction to the extent necessary for the collective interest.[9]

Practically speaking, of course, political and social constraints are likely to make the adoption by governments of any but the most indirect measures to affect individual decisions about family size impossible in the foreseeable future.

There is nothing about family-planning programs that would prevent the addition of legal sanctions or incentives at a later time, however. Dr. William McElroy has replied to suggestions made by Dr. Davis:

> Programs of social change must operate within the framework of existing values, and few governments are yet pre-

> pared to adopt stringent economic or social means to bring down birth rates. (If tried, they would probably be more likely to bring down the government!)
>
> . . . We do agree that every effort should be made to develop additional policies that will support present family-planning programs. Such supplements need to be acceptable and workable within present and likely political, economic, and social reality, but, as Davis properly argues, they need not require unquestioning acceptance of the status quo.[10]

It is clear that in the present social context, government programs must be catalytic rather than the total effort. Formal policy statements at high governmental levels are neither necessary nor sufficient to achieve a reduction in fertility. In some rapidly developing areas of Asia such as Singapore, Hong Kong, and Taiwan, widespread contraceptive practices antedated official policy. The role of governments in reducing fertility is to exhort, inform, and provide; decisions and actions must be taken by couples acting within their perceived interests. The governmental task is, nevertheless, large and difficult, requiring a high degree of organization, adequate financial and logistic support, and continuing evaluation of results.

Even newer contraceptive measures such as the pill and the IUD may be inadequate for poorly motivated or illiterate people. More research and technological effort to develop better birth-control methods are needed to speed up family planning programs. There needs to be more emphasis on birth-control education in *all* countries. The importance of education is not simply in facilitating the dissemination of knowledge about the means of birth control; it is the fact that educated people become involved with modern ideas and institutions. If the individual sees himself as part of a larger, non-familial system, he begins to find rewards in social and economic relationships in which a large number of children may be unnecessary or even a hindrance.

Unquestionably, religious doctrine plays a part in population policy, although an examination of the data does not bear out that religion carries any more weight than other social and cultural factors. Despite criticism, some of it justified, of the 1968 Papal Encyclical, Catholic birth rates in Europe are among the world's lowest and those in Latin America among the highest.

Catholic families tend to be larger than non-Catholic families, but this is not due to lack of knowledge about contraception but because the desired family size is larger. Devout Afrikaans-Protestants have large families, and despite the fact that the Moslem religion has no ban on contraception, it operates under the principle that "Allah will provide." As Dr. Hellegers has put it, "The point is that the religio-cultural perception of one's duties in the field of procreation does not always agree with specific church doctrines on contraception, whether they are permissive or restrictive."[11]

There are few problems that have received more attention in terms of rhetoric. A declaration on Population by World Leaders was presented by Secretary-General U Thant of the United Nations on Human Rights Day in December of 1966. President Lyndon B. Johnson called for U.S. support of family planning in his 1965 State of the Union message, and within the next three years he referred to the population problem publicly on at least forty-four occasions. Robert McNamara, President of the World Bank, gave a major address at Notre Dame University on the population problem in May of 1969. President Richard Nixon has sent a special message to Congress on the subject of the population explosion. Despite all of this talk, the hard *fact* is that the resources devoted to solving this crucial problem are paltry and parsimonious. The total funds spent annually on the population crisis outside the

United States amount to about $80 million. The nations of the world spent nearly $155 billion in 1966 for military purposes. The world spends $2,000 preparing for war for every $1 it spends to control the population explosion.[12] It is hard to imagine a more incredible or tragic confusion of priorities.

The "population problem" is ordinarily thought of in terms of *numbers* of people, but the *distribution* of a country's population is also of crucial importance. Dr. Philip Hauser has referred to the immigration into cities as the "population implosion." The difficulties created by shifts in the United States population are well known and are coming to constitute one of the major domestic social problems of our time.

The growth of large cities is a well-recognized characteristic of developed nations, but it is not generally recognized that the trend toward urbanization is fully as strong in the developing countries. As early as 1950, more than one-third of the world's cities with populations exceeding 100,000 were in Asia, and the exodus from rural areas has accelerated each year since. In Taiwan, one of the more rapidly developing nations, the number of farmers declined from 49 to 38 percent of the labor force between 1965 and 1969, with the result that some areas face a shortage of farm labor and the area of land planted in winter rice has begun to decrease.[13] Mechanization is an obvious solution to this unusual situation of shortage of rural labor, but farm machinery is still too expensive for most Taiwanese farmers. A power-tiller costs $1,500, more than the average farmer earns in four years. It appears that long-term government loans will be required to meet the need.

The enormous increase in non-farm population in the diet-deficient countries has aggravated the food problem further by making it necessary to develop distribution systems to move more and more food into the cities from the producing areas. This requires the establishment of transportation, storage, processing, and marketing facilities on an unprecedented scale in economies which are already stretched to their limits.

The shift of people from farms to cities in the United States and Western Europe has resulted primarily from the reduction in rural labor requirements brought about by advances in modern agricultural technology and increased labor requirements of industry. In the developing countries population growth alone has heightened the frequency with which families leave the overcrowded poverty-stricken countryside, hoping to find a livelihood in the city. The results in many nations have been growing slums and unemployment, since unskilled labor is overabundant in both rural and urban areas.

Because governments in developing countries have paid attention to cities rather than the countryside, since the political base for their power resides in cities, their policies have been to foster slum-clearance projects, sewage and water systems, large buildings, and highways leading to and from cities. All of this tends to intensify the influx of the population, and creates what the Paddock brothers have called the "physical drag of the city" on development. It is estimated that at least 85 percent of external economic aid has been spent on cities rather than on creating the means to boost agricultural production. As the Paddocks put it:

> When the civil disorders build up from rising food prices, the leaders will have this mental block that first, beyond all else, they must keep the city people quiet. As the prime national policy, this will surely be a foundation of sand on which to build programs aimed to save the nation.[14]

So much for the population problem. It is incredibly complex and controversial. It is gross and it is subtle. It is subject to objective mathematical analysis and is charged with emotion. It encompasses the most intimate details of the private life of the individual and the most basic aspects of public policy for societal progress. Robert McNamara has summarized the situation in ringing terms:

> What we must comprehend is this: the population problem *will* be solved one way or the other. Our only fundamental option is whether it is to be solved rationally and humanely—or irrationally and inhumanely. Are we to solve it by famine? Are we to solve it by riot, by insurrection, by the violence that desperately starving men can be driven to? Are we to solve it by wars or expansion and aggression? Or are we to solve it rationally, humanely—in accord with man's dignity?[15]

As a nation, the United States entered the economic assistance field in earnest under President Truman's famous Point Four. We were full of confidence and enthusiasm, fresh from the heady successes of the Marshall Plan in Europe. In Europe, however, there already existed long-established, highly developed credit institutions for banking, marketing, transportation, and agriculture. There was no shortage of seasoned managerial talent and there was a large reservoir of skilled workmen ready to man the machines as soon as they could be provided.

In the developing nations, however, the job has turned out to be *tough,* incredibly more complicated, difficult, and prolonged than anyone imagined in the beginning. This new task, we found, did not entail merely the restoration of a bruised economy like our own, but required the *building of a new structure from the ground up.*

The hard fact remains that despite expenditures of billions of dollars for foreign aid; despite donations and concessional sales of millions of tons of food to developing nations; despite herculean efforts by numerous voluntary groups, despite examples of highly productive technical assistance programs by foundations; and despite years of activity by international organizations such as the World Bank, the United

Nations Food and Agriculture Organization (FAO), the World Health Organization (WHO), the United Nations Educational, Scientific and Cultural Organization (UNESCO), and the United Nations International Children's Emergency Fund (UNICEF), there are today in the world more hungry mouths than ever before in history.

The Third World Food Survey of the FAO in 1963 estimated that 20 percent of the population in the developing countries was undernourished and that 60 percent received diets of less than adequate vitamin or protein content. Protein-calorie malnutrition, which primarily affects preschool children, is the most widespread deficiency.

Despite its complexity, the problem, at first glance, seems deceptively straightforward and is, therefore, unusually susceptible to oversimplification. Because, as I have mentioned, farming seems readily understandable to the average citizen in a developed country such as the United States, where the scientific base of modern agriculture is taken for granted, the temptation to act on the basis of superficial or incomplete information has been irresistible. This has led to seizure and overemphasis upon panaceas and piecemeal "solutions" which are inapplicable, ineffectual, or inadequate. The cumulative delays engendered by false starts and stop-gap measures have obscured the requirement for broad and effective programs, tailored to the demands and dimensions of the over-all problem.

There is no panacea. Periodically, the news media draw attention to ongoing research on systems which offer possibilities as new sources of human food. Because there is a strong tendency to portray these as possible "solutions" to the world food problem and because the public is drawn understandably to such panaceas, the publicity undoubtedly lessens concern about the seriousness of the food supply in the developing nations.

The World Food Panel examined carefully and in detail the several new processes for "unconventional food" that are under current study. "Single cell protein" derived from fermentation by yeasts or bacteria of carbohydrates, hydrocarbons, or cellulose is particularly promising. A great advantage of single-cell protein is that it can be produced independently of agriculture or climatic conditions. However, there are major unsolved problems of scale of production, processing characteristics, nutritive quality, consumer acceptance, and cost which remain to be worked out. It will be several years, *at least,* before a decision concerning the possible usefulness of such materials in the food supply can be made.

Methods for extraction of protein from green leaves have been devised and deserve careful consideration and further research, since the materials utilized are frequently wasted or fed to animals. Again, many problems of nutritive quality, scale, cost, and acceptability must be solved before evaluation of the over-all usefulness of this material will be possible.

Investigations of the usefulness of algae as human food have been unrewarding thus far because of the excessive cost of devising a product that is safe for human consumption. It now appears that the usefulness of algae materials, economically derived as a by-product of reclaiming sewage and other waste waters, will be as a feed for livestock.

A process for producing fish protein concentrate (FPC) has received great publicity in recent years. It appears to hold some promise for the future, although major problems of scale, technologies for different species, and consumer acceptability must be solved before its usefulness can be evaluated.

In summary, some nonconventional sources of food appear to offer great potential for the long term, but none of these can be expected to lessen the problem of increasing food production from conventional sources during the next two decades. Furthermore, the magnitude of the world's food problem is so great that nonconventional sources, when and if they become available, will be needed to *supplement* rather than *supplant* modernized agriculture.

The details of the task involved in increasing food production to meet world needs have never been charted with the clarity and exactness that the available information will permit. The problem has been treated dramatically but incompletely—usually to incite short-term action for humanitarian reasons. A wholehearted response to an *incomplete proposal*, however, lulls the participants into an unjustified feeling of security that the problem is coming under control.

There is no more striking example of this attitude than the reaction to the starvation of children in the Nigerian civil war. Commenting on this in *The Washington Post* last year, S. S. Rosenfeld wrote:

> ... The world's response to the Nigerian tragedy is relief, a quick burst of humanitarianism. . . . Yet, however emotionally necessary the provision of relief is to the donors, it is physically inadequate to the recipients. Hunger in Nigeria, like hunger everywhere, is too profound to be left to the intermittent impulse of charity. It can be properly approached only in institutional ways: more food, more population control, more development, more self-help, more aid.[16]

The episode of the "Biafra Christmas Ship" bears out the futility of these "quick bursts of humanitarianism." A drive to collect food and medicines for Biafra in the New York area attracted thousand of donors, but the 300 tons of food collected and shipped never reached Biafra and remained on the docks at a small island off the African coast where it went uneaten because the food was so ill-suited to Biafran tastes or needs. Among the abandoned cargo were; rice cereals, strawberry and vanilla puddings, custard mixtures, chocolate mousse, pie-crust mixes, cocktail cheese tasties, noodles, spaghetti, ravioli, ketchup, sweet pickles, and barbecue sauce! It was soon dubbed "the pudding ship." Hugh Lloyd of the World Council of Churches commented: "The pudding ship would be something straight out of Gilbert and Sullivan if it weren't so senseless." Wilfred Gunther, the official receiving agent for relief shipments, said: "From the relief point of view, more than 70 percent of the . . . cargo is totally unacceptable. When you figure the price of transport and storage and what the food cost in the first place, we could have bought 1,000 tons of stockfish. So many people have shown so much goodwill in donating this stuff. But the entire enterprise put sentiment before reason."

Food shortage and rapid population growth are separate, but interrelated problems. The solutions, likewise, are separate, but related. The choice is not to solve one or the other; to solve *both* is an absolute necessity. The current tendency to think of food production and fertility control as alternative solutions to a common problem is dangerously misleading.

The twin problems of food and population imbalance have one feature in common that adds immeasurably to the difficulties of achieving control. Their eventual solution is crucially dependent upon success in convincing millions of citizens in the developing nations to take *individual* action. Fertility control cannot be achieved by declarations of government policy or by executive decree, although adoption of a policy and the provision of information, instruction, and materials are obviously needed and are helpful. Similarly, political declarations concerning agricultural productivity are ineffective unless individual farmers can be convinced to adopt the necessary improved practices. The provision of these *personal* incentives is a task that encompasses a vast array of social, economic, and political considerations which differ between countries and within countries. Indeed, the very fabric of traditional societies must be rewoven if the situation is to change permanently.

The receptivity and toleration of people and their political systems require mutual calculation and recalculation. The rates and magnitudes of United States economic assistance programs have been said to "run headlong into nineteenth-century banking systems, eighteenth-century commercial codes, corporate arrangements based on familial ownership, and investment attitudes of a low-risk, high-yield, short-term nature like mercantilist seventeenth-century England."

These conflicting elements of many centuries make it clear that the world is unlikely to obey Richardson's architectural prescription that form should follow function. During the past two decades we have had many lessons in accommodating ourselves to the unwelcome facts that what we call *leadership* may be viewed by others as *exploitation,* what we call *help* may be viewed as *interference,* and what we call *assistance* may be viewed as *intervention.* We call it the Rio Grande; the Mexicans call it the Rio Bravo. We consider ourselves to be a Good Neighbor; many of them think of us as the "Colossus of the North." As Dictator Porfirio Diaz used to say: "Poor Mexico: so far from God, so close to the United States."

In agricultural development as well as in other areas of assistance to a developing country, the political stability and predominant attitudes of the recipient government are of crucial importance. Most American citizens are thoroughly familiar with the constraints and disruptions that domestic political conditions within a developing country can create for aid programs. Recent history is replete with episodes which try our patience and frustrate our good intentions.

In contrast to these more obvious and better-publicized difficulties at the political level, the obstacles posed by traditional culture, social structure, religious beliefs, and the long-established habits and customs of many developing countries are rarely considered in truly realistic terms. To understand, much less to accept these constraints is particularly difficult for Americans who remain among the citizens of Western nations the least cosmopolitan and least tolerant of delay. The problem of ethnological differences has been epitomized by Francis E. Dart:

> In one country, steel plows are introduced where previously a pointed stick had served. The farmers accepted them with polite gratitude and use them as ornaments, but not for plowing. Why? These plows require two hands, and the farmers are accustomed to using only one, the other being used to guide the bullock. A more productive variety of rice cannot be introduced in part of Nepal, where it is needed and very well suited to climate and soil, because the grains cling a bit more to the stalk and a new threshing technique would have to be used. But threshing is a family or community undertaking involving social and ritual as well as mechanical activities. Running water in people's houses is not accepted because the village well is a social center, as well as source of water. . . . It would not be difficult to put together a large list of such minor failures nor to include in it some major ones. If these seem improbable or easily overcome, the reader might review the introduction of an innovation, say the fluoridation of water, into our own technologically highly sophisticated society. He might also consider the willingness with which Christians, out of Christian motives, will help to reduce infant mortality and disease in a distant, non-Christian country and how unwilling they may be then to help control the population explosion that inevitably results.[17]

An important facet of this problem, often overlooked, has to do with food customs and taboos. It is easy to forget, when discussing tonnages of proteins and millions of calories that, in the final analysis, the commodity must be made available to the consumer as a food product which he will *eat.* Dietary habits are established early in life and, in the highly traditional cultures of many developing countries, food selection and diet more often reflect religious and social beliefs than they do the principles of human nutrition. During the past several years, there have been many commercial programs intended to make unfamiliar new food products available to low-income groups in the developing countries. It has become abundantly clear that it is extremely difficult to change fixed food habits. Market research and feasibility studies must give proper attention both to family income and existing habits and taboos. It has been demonstrated that dietary customs *can* be changed (e. g., people whose dietary staple has been rice have been persuaded to take wheat as a supplement or substitute), but success in any such undertaking requires time and a carefully prepared program of consumer education. Any program to remedy malnutrition which involves changing traditional food habits is highly likely to be ineffective in the short-run, and even a long-range plan must be carefully programmed for the specific local situation. There is a renewed emphasis upon supplementing traditional foods by addition of amino acids, vitamins, or minerals to keep down costs and to circumvent the problem of new foods.

Considerable success has been achieved by using protein of various types in beverages in various parts of the world. Indeed, this is now one of the more hopeful approaches to correcting malnutrition without the need to change food habits and preferences completely.

It is evident that the bulk of the increase in food supply must come from increased production of farm crops. There are two ways in which agricultural production can be increased: by bringing more land under cultivation or by increasing yields of land under cultivation. Until recently, most of the increase in food production in the developing countries has been achieved by extending traditional farming methods over a larger area of cropland. Substantial opportunities remain to bring additional land under cultivation in the less densely populated areas of Latin America and of Africa, but the vast majority of arable land in Asia is already in use. While there are marginal possibilities for using small additional areas, it is clear that as the population continues to grow, the amount of cropland per person in the Asian countries will diminish progressively.

In Asia, a shift to increasing crop production by intensifying agriculture and using modern methods to improve annual yields on land under cultivation will be mandatory. Even in Latin America and Africa, the increasing cost of clearing additional land may well make it more economical in many regions to concentrate on elevating yields rather than expanding cultivated areas.

To increase yields, a major expansion of irrigation facilities will be necessary to make multiple cropping possible, independent of wide variations in seasonal rainfall. It will also be necessary to develop and utilize new, high-yielding plant varieties, to develop and utilize plants with a higher quality of protein, to increase the use of fertilizers and pesticides, and to use improved farm machinery (not to save labor but to increase yields and actually to allow increased employment at farm work). Increased capital investments and increased expenditure on the part of farmers will be required to make these tools of modern agriculture available. These are the techniques that have been employed so successfully in the developed countries to transform farming into a *business.*

This transition to modern agriculture will be difficult and expensive for the hungry nations, but it is absolutely essential if their food needs are to be met. There is no alternative.

It is of utmost importance to emphasize that a modern agicultural system involves more than those activities which take place upon the farm. The problem of hunger is not merely one of *production.* The *distribution* of food to those who need it is the final objective of any solution to the problem. Until now, a majority of efforts in the developing countries have been aimed at improving the farm production of food crops. This has consisted of developing new plant varieties which will respond well to fertilizer and will convert a larger amount of energy into edible grain. The best-known examples of these new plants are the "dwarf wheats" developed by the Rockefeller Foundation in Mexico and the "miracle rice" developed by the International Rice Research Institute in the Philippines. The use of these varieties in India and in Pakistan during the past two years has given remarkable increases in the wheat and rice harvests in certain regions. This has led to a state approaching euphoria on the part of political leaders and a great deal of rhetoric about the breakthrough accompanying the so-called Green Revolution.

These improvements in farm production are certainly encouraging, and their importance should not be minimized. They are not, however, a signal for relaxation of effort. Lester R. Brown, former Administrator of the U.S. Department of Agriculture's International Agricultural Development Service and a self-admitted optimist concerning the food-population problem, has pointed out that these initial successes in production have generated a series of "second generation" problems connected with marketing, storage, distribution, and the question of how millions of small subsistence farmers are going to be able to employ the new agricultural technologies.

The socio-political conflicts that are likely to arise in these areas are what Brown calls "problems of success."[18]

Others have warned against overoptimism about the Green Revolution:

> India's agricultural progress of the last two years has convinced the most cautious observers that it is well within the bounds of technological feasibility for her to feed her swelling population.... India need never experience another famine, they say.
>
> But the fact of hunger remains painfully real, for the gap between promise and achievement has only begun to narrow....
>
> It is apparent that sustaining the green revolution and extending it . . . will require tremendous resources, far-sighted planning, and social reforms. The technology is increasingly plentiful, but resources, decisions, and reforms remain scarce....[19]

Some idea of the magnitude of the "second-generation problems" brought about by the initial successes of the Green Revolution is illustrated in an analysis of India's problems of transport, storage, and marketing carried out by Olen W. Salisbury of the U. S. Department of Agriculture in 1968. Salisbury estimated that India would produce a total of 120 million metric tons of foodgrains by 1973, of which 70 percent would be consumed in the rural areas and 30 percent—thirty-six million tons—would be purchased, transported, stored, and sold in urban centers throughout the nation. He points out vividly what handling thirty-six million tons of grain will entail:

> To provide perspective consider the question; what is thirty-six million tons of foodgrains? In terms of gunnies it is 360,000,000, which, if laid end to end, would girdle the earth eight times at the equator. In terms of railway wagons it is 1,500,000 wagon loads. In terms of lorries (trucks) it is 6,000,000 lorry loads. In terms of farmer sales transactions at the present average of four quintals (400 Kilos) per sale it is 90,000,000 individual sales transactions. In terms of storage space it is more than 2,000,000,000 cubic feet....

> Transport data available is as of March 31, 1966, which indicated 228,179 licensed lorries and 163,207 covered railway wagons. If six tons is an effective average load estimate for a lorry then each lorry would be required to make twenty-four trips, or each railway wagon would be utilized ten times for the movement of thirty-six million tons of foodgrains. During the ten-year period 1955–56 to 1965–66 the rail tonnage of foodgrains increased from 3.2 million to 6.8 million tons or slightly more than 100 percent. This volume taxed facilities, and it must be remembered that a substantial part was represented by imports received in large volume at major ports where equipment is more readily available than it is in the hinterland. Even if this rate of increase continued by 1970–71, the rails presumably could handle 10.2 million tons or less than one-third of the projected thirty-six million tons, leaving 25.8 million tons for movement by highway.[20]

It seems very clear that there is no possibility that Indian transport facilities will be able to handle the projected volume of grain and that a high rate of loss of the increased harvest by spoilage will be inevitable. It is also likely that government procurement programs designed to stabilize markets will have to be geared to the *transport availability* of grain rather than the *farm availability* of the harvest. It is difficult to see how it would be politically possible to use public funds to purchase commodities which will spoil because of lack of facilities for transport and storage.

This is but one example of the secondary problems posed by the Green Revolution. For a more detailed and perceptive analysis of the broad range of issues to be confronted, the reader is referred to Clifton R. Wharton's discussion in *Foreign Affairs.*[21]

Unless farmers in a traditional subsistence agriculture can be persuaded (that is, can be supplied with *incentives*) to use fertilizer, pesticides, seeds, and the other modern inputs to increase output, *all other efforts to increase food production will fail.* Until a "cash flow" can be generated at farm level, agricultural development will be stymied. Inputs cost money; farmers need credit to buy them; farmers need to be able to sell their products at a price that will enable them to pay for inputs and have something left besides. When price policy holds down food costs for the consumer, the producer may not get his share and, hence, may see no reason to produce beyond the immediate needs of his family. In many of the developing countries, the lands are cultivated by tradition-bound peasants who are controlled by a political system which has its power base in cities and is unfamiliar or unconcerned with problems of farming or with the measures, including price incentives, needed to increase agricultural productivity.

Most Americans are at least somewhat familiar with the recurrent difficulties of assuring adequate payment to farm producers in the United States, particularly since modern technology has reduced the number of farm workers and, hence, their political importance.

Many of Soviet Russia's difficulties with agricultural production are related to farmer incentives. Even when farmers can make a profit, unless consumer goods which they wish to purchase are available, the money means little to them, and one of the persisting Soviet problems (although by no means the only one) is to make consumer goods available in the rural areas. This need is but one of the many reasons that the agricultural and industrial sectors must grow together in developing countries; they are *complementary,* not *competitive.*

Farming is a business, and, in the last analysis, the rate of increased production in agriculture is determined by effective market demand. In other words, it costs money to produce food just as it costs money to produce any other commodity, and someone must pay the bill for an increase in output.

There are relationships between the demand for foodstuffs and the over-all demand for goods and services in any economy. In order for "effective demand" for food to exist, the means of buying the food—purchasing power—must be available.

Likewise, on the supply or production side, there are relationships which link agricultural food production to over-all production. Farms require manufactured inputs such as fertilizer, pesticides, and machinery which must be imported or produced domestically. If they are imported, the over-all economy must generate sufficient exports or rely on a net inflow of foreign assistance or private capital to pay for the imports. If these inputs are produced domestically or paid for by industrial exports, the non-agricultural sectors must expand at rates consistent with the need of the agricultural sector. Various non-agricultural sectors are dependent on agricultural raw materials and, in some cases, food products.

Because of the interdependence which exists among food need, food demand, over-all income, agricultural output, and total output (which is G.N.P.), it is meaningless to consider a nation's demand for and supply of foodstuffs independently from over-all economic growth.

The very nature of farming must be understood if appropriate measures are to be developed in the hungry nations. Farm production is based upon the growth processes of plants that utilize solar energy through photosynthesis. Because the basic process of farming depends upon solar energy, it must always remain widely distributed over the face of the earth so the sunlight can be utilized where it falls. *No other single fact has greater significance for agricultural development.* On the one hand, it requires an extensive and well-articulated transportation system to move the production inputs which a progressive agriculture needs from distant points of manufacture to each farm and to move farm products to ultimate consumers. Furthermore, it denies to farming two opportunities that are available to many other industries. One of these is the opportunity to concentrate activities in order that industries geographically adjacent can exchange products, avoiding major transportation costs or time lags. The other is the opportunity to create favorable working conditions without transforming an entire society. A steel or textile mill can establish working conditions in a plant which, during working hours, will separate laborers from the demands, customs, and traditions of their families. Agriculture cannot do this, since farming must be carried on in widely dispersed village settings, in the midst of family influences and traditional social pressures. Agricultural development, by virtue of this inherent dispersal, requires a *major social transformation.* It cannot create in part-time oases the new sets of working conditions appropriate to its production needs.

Some idea of the magnitude of the transportation task in a modern agricultural system is illustrated by the estimate that in 1964–65, ninety-four million tons of farm supplies and equipment were moved into the commercial farms of the U.S. and 324 million tons of farm products moved from these farms to markets, an average of 11,500 pounds per acre.

The relationship between transportation and the ability to grow and market food has been demonstrated repeatedly. When the hundred-mile-long "Friendship Highway" in Thailand reduced travel time from eleven hours on the old road to three on the new, the production of sugar cane, bananas, and other fruits more than tripled in three years and Thailand began to export corn to Japan.

In advanced Western countries, there are from three to four miles of farm access roads per square mile of cultivated land. In India, the average now is 0.7 mile and it will require about 1,000,000 miles of access roads to satisfy the needs of the 580,000 villages throughout the country. Only 11 percent now have adequate roads and one out of three is more than five miles from a satisfactory road.

Particularly in the field of agricultural development, *technical assistance* is essential to achieving the ultimate objective of foreign aid—namely, self-sustaining economic growth.

There still persists in many quarters the feeling that research or science is a sort of luxury or prestige activity which has no substantial place in a program of aid to developing countries. Quite apart from the fact that adaptive research is an absolute prerequisite to the use of modern agricultural systems in different regions of the world, the basis for continuing agricultural development in *any* country, including the United States, is continuing research. Research in modern agriculture is a never-ending task.

Improvement of agricultural production by modern scientific methods consists of *adapting* plant varieties, pesticides, fertilizer usage, and cropping techniques to the local soil and climate. In other words, a "package" is tailor-made for the locality by applying scientific principles to find the answers to local problems. Just as one size of uniform cannot be expected to fit all soldiers, the final fit depending upon tailoring the garment to the individual, no single set of agricultural technology can be transferred successfully to another country without tailoring it by adaptive research. Furthermore, the adaptive research and testing must be carried out in the country or region where crop improvement is desired.

The failure of most of us, including policy-makers in government, to distinguish between the ability of agriculture science to find answers and already knowing the answers has led to insufficient emphasis upon technical assistance as opposed to "practical assistance." For example, a so-called farmer-to-farmer program has been proposed and enacted into law in the well-intentioned but quite erroneous belief that American farmers could be sent overseas to teach farmers in the developing countries how to increase farm production. Without the scientific and technological back-up routinely available to them in the United States, these farmers would be helpless to change conditions elsewhere. Agriculturalists have repeatedly tried to correct this "know-how, show-how" fallacy by saying that what works in Kansas won't work in Karachi; but the message has not yet penetrated foreign-aid policy to the required extent, and the notion that research is an absolute necessity rather than an academic diversion is very slow to disappear from popular thinking.

Increasingly, United States foreign assistance should take the form of knowledge, technical aid, adaptive research, education, and institution-building. The scarcest and most needed resource in the developing countries is the scientific, technical, and managerial skill needed for systematic, orderly decision-making and implementation. Through technical-assistance programs, the United States should emphasize guidance, education, and the development of indigenous capabilities—for the long term—because the task in the developing nations will continue for decades to come.

A World Health Organization publication, *Malnutrition and Disease,* ends on a note of quiet dispair:

> Moreover, the lesson of history is that effective control of birth rate on a community scale has only followed the development of material wealth and a high standard of literacy. An increasing population, in the presence of static or even decreasing possibilities of food production, gives rise to the most desperately urgent and widespread problem today, hunger and chronic undernourishment.

The response to this which I heard from a veteran worker in the field of international development was:

> History has said a lot of things it took back later—for example, that man cannot fly. Our job is not only to study history but to help make it!

An editorial in *The Christian Science Monitor,* entitled *World Poverty Circle,* described what is perhaps the greatest obstacle of all to economic development in the poor nations. Quoting a recent statement by John Kenneth Galbraith that economic expansion in the United States no longer is hampered by a shortage of money, but rather by a shortage of qualified manpower, the editorial goes on to say:

> It is, however, in weighing America's problems in this direction that one gets a clearer picture of the difficult situation which faces so many nations today as they seek to propel themselves forward economically. For, while American establishments sometimes find themselves short of trained personnel, how infinitely better off are they than those establishments in so many other lands which have neither trained personnel nor the hope of adequate financing.
>
> With either trained personnel or sufficient financing, a country is able to begin that self-perpetuating upward spiral of development which leads to a steadily broadening economy and rising standard of living. Trained manpower always generates money. And money can greatly ease the task of producing trained manpower.
>
> But without either, a country often does little more than go round and round on the same dead-level circle, producing neither wealth nor a class of citizenry well enough educated and skilled to break out of the circle. In most of Africa, throughout much of Latin America and over wide areas of Asia this is the situation which prevails today.
>
> The Afro-Asian-Latin American problem is compounded by the fact that, even when progress is made in either accumulating investable wealth or in enlarging the reservoir of educated men and women, this is offset by the increase in population, which, in turn, creates new problems.

At some point a means must be found to break up the self-perpetuating circle of poverty—too many people, too few skills, too little money.

Until technical-assistance programs have been successful in establishing within the developing countries the institutional and manpower bases for continued research in agriculture, in health, in all aspects of physical, biological, and social sciences, and in administration, management, and techniques of diffusing knowledge, no amount of capital investment alone will succeed in bringing about self-sustained economic growth in these nations.

The hard-won experience of the past two decades and the urgent problem of feeding the burgeoning millions in the developing countries, taken together, signal the need and the opportunity for a re-orientation and expansion of the United States program of economic assistance. We should minimize the errors of the past and, in concert with other nations, apply the knowledge that we have acquired by strenuous and dedicated effort.

The increasing use of multilateral assistance is not a new idea, of course. The size and duration of the effort that will be required to cope with the problem of the world food supply will necessitate a strengthening and restructuring of the existing United Nations agencies, many of which are not geared to operational efforts on the scale that will be required. Bilateral effort should be maintained and expanded by the developed countries, particularly in technical assistance and in programs involving the private sector of the economy. The willingness of universities and business firms to increase their activities in the developing countries will be better preserved and expanded through bilateral programs.

Such efforts should be planned on a basis of long-term *strategy.* Their continuity should not be subject to threat from episodic disagreements among nations, and withdrawal or curtailment should not be employed as a foreign-policy sanction except under the gravest of international crises.

The agencies charged with this task must have a new capacity to measure economic and agricultural development and hence understand the food-supply problem. It is essential to develop a system to examine all the elements required to deal with this complex situation and permit the drafting of coordinated programs to be carried on throughout the world. One way in which this critically important function could be accomplished would be through a non-profit international planning organization. Such a group could undertake this task of measurement, appraisal, planning, programming, and monitoring results. The extraordinary technological resources now available in developed countries can be creatively applied to this immense problem.

The United States should assume leadership of the free world and all of its international institutions in a coordinated, long-range development strategy for raising the economic level of the poor nations, thereby meeting the threat of hunger, increasing the volume of world trade and economic activity, and contributing to the achievement of the goal of ultimate importance, lasting peace and dignity for all mankind.

Unfortunately, this is not yet the choice of America. The resources allocated to foreign aid diminish each year. The latest budget proposal for economic assistance is the lowest in the twenty-year history of the program and, as has become routine in recent years, it is threatened by substantial additional cuts in the Congress.

This will remain the situation until the American people are convinced that to help the developing nations is an effort which merits investment of their taxes and that the effort will be effective in achieving its purpose.

The reasons that the citizens of the United States should

be concerned with the hungry nations are threefold:

1. *Humanitarian.* We should help the less fortunate simply because they need help and we are able to help them. The benefits of altruism are by no means unilateral. The challenge of a difficult task and the moral uplift that comes only from doing for others are needed to temper and balance the leisure and affluence of American life. The real successes of the Peace Corps center in the fundamentally inspired, collective aim that is exemplified in the late Albert Schweitzer's dictum, "It is only giving that stimulates."

2. *Security.* By the year 2000, if present rates of growth continue, there will be more than four times as many people in the developing countries as are in the developed nations. To avoid a threat to the peace of the world as well as to our own national security, we cannot afford to be too little and too late with our development assistance. The expectations of the poor are demanding fulfillment. It is to be hoped that some measure of their ambitions can be realized by peaceful means.

3. *A Better Tomorrow for Us, Too.* This is a long-range goal, an economic reason for investment. An important way to expand our own economy in the future will be through further specialization and trade. As nations develop, they become trading nations and, through trade, both parties to a transaction benefit. Trading partners are likely to be peaceful protagonists. This last reason has important implications for the inclusion of trade concessions in our program of assistance. Trade adjustments which appear to involve immediate sacrifices may, in the longer view, be far less costly than capital assistance given in the traditional fashion. It is highly likely, in most instances, that provision of export markets based upon competitive advantage will be a most effective stimulus to development.

All too often, the wealthy nations have seemed to regard economic assistance as a short-term relief to countries which are temporarily poor. The experience of the past two decades indicates that aid should become a part of a concept of the economic relations between unequally developed countries, which will last for many decades to come.

NOTES

1. *The World Food Problem, A Report of the President's Science Advisory Committee,* 3 vol., The White House, 1967.
2. Shabecoff, P.: *Jakarta Seeks Modest Economic Revolution, The New York Times,* Feb. 19, 1969.
3. Report on the Lembaga Ilmu Pengetahuan Indonesia-National Academy of Sciences, USA, Workshop on Food, May, 1968, Vol. III, page 54.
4. Hardin, L.: *Our Stake in Economic Development,* Address at Purdue University, March 15, 1967.
5. Galphin, B.: "Senators Find Food Alone Won't Solve Misery of Poor," *The Washington Post,* March 16, 1969.
6. Lindner, F.: Testimony on *Population Crisis,* January 31, 1968, Senate Subcommittee on Foreign Aid Expenditures, 90th Congress, Second Session, U. S. Government Printing Office, Washington, 1968, page 461.
7. Hellegers, A. E.: "Factors and Correctives in Population Expansion," *SAIS Review,* The Johns Hopkins School of Advanced International Relations, Spring, 1969.
8. Brandt, K.: *Famine Is Not Inevitable,* Report No. 7, The Victor Fund for The International Planned Parenthood Federation, Fall, 1967.
9. Davis, K.: *Will Family Planning Solve the Population Problem?* The Victor-Bostrom Fund Report No. 10, Fall, 1968.
10. McElroy, W.: *Will Family Planning Solve the Population Problem?* The Victor-Bostrom Fund Report No. 10, Fall, 1968.
11. Hellegers, A. E., *op. cit.*
12. Wicker, T.: "In the Nation: Population, Hunger and Oblivion," *The New York Times,* May 4, 1968.
13. Butterfield, F.: "Movement Off Farms in Taiwan Threatens Agricultural Growth," *The New York Times,* August 31, 1969.

14. Paddock, W. and Paddock, P.: *Famine-1975!,* Little, Brown and Company, Boston, 1967.
15. McNamara, R. S.: *Address to the University of Notre Dame,* May 1, 1969 (International Bank for Reconstruction and Development, Washington, D.C.).
16. Rosenfeld, S. S.: "Hunger in Biafra: World Harbinger," *The Washington Post,* October 25, 1968.
17. Dart, F. E.: "The Rub of Cultures," *Foreign Affairs,* January 1963, p. 365.
18. Brown, L.R.: "The Optimistic Outlook for World Food Production," *The Futurist,* August, 1969, p. 89.
19. Lelyveld, J.: " 'Green Revolution' Transforming Indian Farming but It Has Long Way to Go," *The New York Times,* May 28, 1969.
20. Salisbury, Olen W.: *Marketing Problems for Indian Foodgrain Production,* Terminal Report, International Agricultural Development Service, Washington, D.C. 20250, April, 1968.
21. Wharton, C.R., Jr.: "The Green Revolution: Cornucopia or Pandora's Box?," *Foreign Affairs,* April, 1969, p. 464.

ETHICS AND THE FAMILY OF MAN

by Dr. Roger L. Shinn

If men were not human, there would be no population problem. More precisely, if men had human ingenuity, but lacked two other human qualities—a concern for what we call the dignity of man and a glorious but stubborn craving for freedom—any problem of population could be easily solved.

In such a world a scientific elite could plan population. It could turn virile men into eunuchs as readily as farmers now turn bulls into steers and stallions into geldings. Or, in a more kindly act of indulgence, it could arrange that men and women have all the delights of sexual relationships except that procreation would be limited. The techniques would require a major, but not an impossible, effort; male and female surgical sterilization, even on a large scale, is technically practicable. The administrators could plan the optimum population and act accordingly. They could, if they chose, add eugenics to their program by a selection of sires and artificial insemination.

Ever since Plato, concerned people have asked why man, who takes some pains in animal breeding, is so much more careless about the far more important business of human breeding. The answer is that just because human breeding is so important, it resists control. People have ethical inhibitions about intruding into the lives of others. And even when the elite lacks inhibitions, the others are stubbornly resistant in asserting their rights of freedom.

So because men are free and human, they live with many problems, including the population problem. Yet because they maintain the freedom to procreate, they are destroying the humanity of many and wounding the humanity of still more. The right to eat and the right to procreate are fundamental human rights; most people regard them as close to rock-bottom rights. But the two have come into conflict. Somehow they must be adjusted to each other. And the adjustment raises profound ethical and theological questions.

The problem is not entirely new. Past societies have dealt with surplus population by (a) exposure of excessive infants and the aged and (b) by conquest of their neighbors, a method that gave more space to the winners and less to the losers, while reducing the numbers of both. All the major civilizations today regard the first solution as inhumane. As for the second, if they are not fully persuaded that it is inhumane, they are pretty well convinced that it is treacherous to all concerned. It *could* end the population problem by eliminating all population, but that is total defeat, not a solution.

Today the old problem has taken on new dimensions so startling as to make it almost a new problem. Traditionally nature, even more than human acts, limited population. Modern man can deal with nature as his ancestors could not. If it is still a little silly to boast about conquering disease and downright silly to boast of conquering death, nevertheless man has won enough battles over disease to make an immense difference. Many more infants survive than in the past, and the age-span of fertility has increased. So the crisis of population is upon us. And the population bomb rivals the nuclear bomb in its threat to mankind.

I. Science and Ethics

Scientific and technical achievement have made the contemporary problem and they offer possibilities for meeting it. The population explosion is a good example of the way in which science (here used broadly to include technique) impinges upon ethics. The natural sciences, strictly conceived, do not dictate ethical conclusions. Even the behavioral sciences lead to ethical judgments only insofar as ethical premises are fed into their processes. But scientific advance changes the behavior of men, their social relations, and their institutions. It has solved for industrial societies once-difficult problems (how to get hot water in the winter and cold water in the summer), while creating new problems that it has not yet solved (how to breathe reasonably pure air in the city, winter or summer). In affluent societies it has made obsolete some human conflicts; we need not struggle over access to springs and wells if we pipe water to everyone. It has created new conflicts—e.g., who shall get the parking space?

Because of science, men are living with some problems that never troubled the past, but they have opportunities unknown to the past. Thus science exerts a profound influence on ethics. It is not enough to say that ethics is a matter of applying constant principles to changing situations. When the very structure of social relations and the set of options open to men are significantly changed, the nature of ethical decision and the working of the ethical imagination change. The technician, whether a sophisticated designer of interplanetary rockets or a taxi driver, must consider the ethical meaning of his acts. And the ethical agent, whether a profound philosopher or a light-hearted adolescent on a date, must make judgments in the light of technical possibilities unknown to his predecessors.

Thus any ethical appraisal of the need for food among the

world's expanding populations must take account of technical developments achieved or anticipated. Even the most traditional and authoritarian ethic, although it may totally reject some available techniques, must count heavily on others; for example, those who renounce contraception have to rely all the more on techniques of food production. Other styles of ethics, less tradition-bound, will pay still more attention to technical achievements. All ethics must move with awareness of possibilities created by modern science.

Yet the ethical problem is never solely technical. Men's decisions about the use of techniques will depend upon their loyalties and human sensitivities. Nowhere is this more the case than in meeting the issues of population.

Nobody worries about the population explosion among chickens. There will be approximately as many chickens as men decide that there will be. Men are slightly less successful in planning the population of cats, still less so in the case of pigeons, and rather unsuccessful in the case of mosquitoes. These examples are reminders that, even in the heady atmosphere of the "conquest" of space, man is not totally master of nature. But in all such cases men work away at technical solutions. If there are some ethical inhibitions about certain types of cruelty to pigeons (probably not to mosquitoes), still society, except for a few old women in tennis shoes, does not draw back in horror from experiments at rendering these creatures sterile.

With human beings, new factors enter into every formula. We must ask of every proposal to order the future not only whether it is technically feasible but also whether it is humanly acceptable. To some extent, ideas of human acceptability change. Many inhibitions are deeply rooted in mores arising out of a past situation, no longer relevant to the present age; men may with good conscience forget them and even undertake with conscientious zeal to urge others to forget them. But ethics is not capricious adaptation. Although it is increasingly hard to define them, there are some root-loyalties that conscientious men are loath to betray. I have already mentioned two that are especially important for the present inquiry: that mysterious quality called human dignity and that equally mysterious power called freedom. To rethink their meaning in a new situation brings a painful crisis in ethics. In such a crisis our generation lives.

II. The Givens and the Indeterminates

At this stage of human history the problem is given: Population growth and food scarcity, long on collision course, have collided. Already two-thirds of the world is underfed. Already 10,000 people a day die from starvation or consequences of malnutrition,[1] as others grow up physically and mentally damaged by inadequate diet in infancy. Statistics are cold. A single starving baby is an atrocity; most of us could not bear the sight. Statistics simply tabulate the desperate experiences and tell us the scope of the problem. Confrontation with the data leads many a scientist—be it said to his credit—to lose his professional cool and become a moral crusader.

In the nature of the case there are two possible remedies, each with indeterminate (but not infinite) possibilities. Food can be increased, and population can be limited. Both are utterly necessary. Either in isolation from the other is a scientific and ethical monstrosity.

Food must be increased because people are starving now. The world is crowded with hungry infants, whose food needs will increase as they grow—that is, as the survivors grow. As Ivan Bennett has shown, "To maintain the Indian population *at its present level* of nutrition would require 20 percent more food in 1975 than in 1965 *if no new children were added during this ten-year period.* To elevate the diet to the minimal standard, recommended by the United Nations Food and Agricultural Organization, a 30 percent increase would be required."[2]

Such facts need to be hammered home, if only because there is a popular disposition to evade the food problem by leaping immediately to the population problem. People usually welcome any rationalization that spares them ethical responsibility; and the population explosion, which is a real and portentous fact, provides a convenient rationalization for many evasions of other problems.

But the contemporary revolution in agriculture, with its stupendous increases in food productivity and its promises of greater miracles yet to come, is also a convenient rationalization for evasion of the population problem. Population growth must be slowed. The fertility of the soil and the sea cannot forever match the fertility of man. An increase in food supplies joined with medical progress, in isolation from restraint in reproduction, saves lives for future breeding and makes a worse problem for the next generation.

This is the point at which the popular projections of population growth are relevant. If the human race continues to double its numbers every thirty-five or so years, arithmetic shows what will happen. The world's population, now between three and four billion, will become seven billion by the year 2000, fifty-six billion by 2105, and so on—and on. According to one reckoning, this process would mean in 900 years a density of 4,550 people for every square foot of the earth's land surface[3]; another reckoning for the same time is 100 persons per square yard of *land and sea.* After some more years, says one physicist, the population would generate so much heat that a "world roof," designed to radiate the heat away, would have to be kept at about the melting point of iron.[4] The same projections can be carried further, until the point where the weight of people exceeds the weight of the solar system —or, in enough more years—the weight of the physical universe.

People frequently dismiss such projections by saying that, of course, no such thing will happen. "Of course" it won't. The critical question, loaded with a freight of moral meaning, concerns what will stop the process. It may be war, pestilence, starvation on an incredible scale, or mass hysteria and insanity —or it may be determined policies of birth control. Such possibilities suggest the nature of the ethical choice before mankind. Ethical choices, at least in the area of public policy, are rarely matters of decision between ideal visions and evil or painful policies. The decisions are between live options with some chance of effectiveness. Today it is evident that mankind cannot maintain forever the present rate of reproduction; to do so is not a possible choice. The choice, then, becomes one of the methods of limiting population. There are methods that, by any criteria of a humane ethic, are preferable to mass destruction of people, whether in mutual slaughter or starvation.

Humanity, then, faces the need of a double course of action: an increase in production and distribution of food and a limitation of man's numbers. On the first of these the Christian imperative is as old as Christian faith. Feeding the hungry is always a good work. On the simplest level, there is no moral problem at all, except the perennial one of overcoming man's greed and hardness of heart. The ethical answer to any question about food for needy people is yes.

But in a complex world, ethical decisions rarely remain on the simplest level. Feeding the hungry, it turns out, is a complicated business. Christians and humanitarians frequently bemoan the facts of agricultural surpluses in America as contrasted with starvation elsewhere. The contrast is appropriate if it sensitizes conscience; we need every help at that point we can get. But to point to the contrast is not to make much contribution to a solution. Food on the Western plains is not food in India or Southeast Asia. If it is to do any good where men are starving, somebody must move it there, must get it to the people who need it, must (sometimes) persuade them that it is edible—and must do all this without ruining the local market so that growers there will raise less next year. Moral idealists may say that the last factor—the market system—is so sordid that it should not count, but to change it requires setting in operation another set of intricately complex forces. To increase food production, apart from general economic development, is largely futile. Of such mundane and brutal facts is ethical action made, and he who refuses to deal in such facts is irresponsible. I say all this to indicate that, even where the traditional ethical imperative is utterly clear, as on feeding the hungry, effective action involves many ethical and technical factors not comprehended by the tradition.

On the second requirement, population control, the Christian imperative is more recent. In fact, the present situation requires some modification, even reversal, of prominent strands in the tradition. Therefore this chapter gives more attention to population than to food.

Traditionally Christians, like people of many other faiths, generally counted large families as a blessing. Some mothers—even some fathers and children—long ago suspected that there could be too much of even this good thing. But, in general, the opinion prevailed that numerous offspring were desirable.

Simultaneously the same tradition included a sex ethic that closely related the sexual act and procreation. In some ways that close relationship was fundamental to the Christian meaning of sex as developed from scripture. But as the ethic was formulated in the West, most influentially by Augustine, sex was so tainted in fallen man that the sexual act was justifiable only if its aim was procreation. Theologians might have found powerful challenges to that doctrine in both Old and New Testaments, but for many centuries few of them did. Today much of the church has broken loose from that belief and has recovered the Biblical awareness that the sexual act has its own good as an expression of conjugal love. (See Jesus' teaching in Mark 10:6–7 and the passages from Genesis 1–2 which he quotes.) The reasons for this change are partly theological, resulting from a reawakening to the message of the Bible and its meaning for man today. They are partly the historical situation to which theology responds, as it always must. In this case the historical situation was not primarily the world population problem but the situation of many Christian families, including sometimes the families of theologians. (Since Protestant theologians more often had families than Catholic theologians, Protestantism moved faster on this issue.) The world population problem certainly has reinforced the concern.

The obvious conspicuous exception, of course, is official Roman Catholicism. Eastern Orthodoxy is less conspicuous, not because it is markedly different from Roman Catholicism, but because it has never centralized the dogmatic teaching authority of the church. But even in Roman Catholicism the recent change has been greater than the persistence in tradition. A generation ago it was common for Catholic moralists to assert that every single act of sexual intercourse, to be moral, must have the intention of procreation. Now no Catholic authority teaches that. The desirability of limiting family size, for the sake of both the family and of society, is recognized. The remaining controversy concerns method. The rhythm method (unfortunately not a very effective method) is officially condoned. Catholic theologians commonly discuss contraception as freely as Protestants or secular humanists.[5] They regard the prejudice against contraceptives as a cultural lag. Regrettably the lag includes the papacy. Pope Paul VI's encyclical, *Huma-*

nae Vitae (July 29, 1968), produced wide dissent at the point of its condemnation of contraceptives. The Pope, in making his judgment, rejected the advice (by a 70-14 vote) of the Papal Commission on Birth Control.[6] If the encyclical produced a crisis, it was not one of sexual ethics but one of the authority of the papacy. Meanwhile, Catholic laymen, sometimes with troubled and sometimes with clear consciences, increasingly abandoned the historic teaching of the Church on this issue, often with the support of their priests.[7] In any case, it had long been evident that Catholic families do not, consistently and on a world-wide basis, have the most babies. (See Part III in this chapter.)

If it was family and world necessity that became the entry point for this discussion, the issues have now broadened. Since there is general agreement that restriction of conception is in some cases a good (whatever the arguments over method), we must ask at what point it is a good. Is it only a last resort, when starvation is present or imminent? Once it is decided that population growth is not an absolute value, it must be weighed among other values—of which food is important, but not alone.

Many a family long ago decided to stop with two or three children, not because another one or two would have starved, but because it could provide more comfort and opportunity for all if the family remained modest in size. An old-fashioned ethic sometimes described this decision as a cold-hearted calculation in contrast to a warm humanity that produced a household brimming with children. To the family involved, the issues were very different. Perhaps the home (and any home the family expected to acquire) could offer reasonable comfort and privacy to two children. Perhaps the parents could help two children to a good education, whereas four would have to scramble for what they could get. Perhaps the father and mother had purposes—good purposes—that meant they should concentrate some major energies on projects other than rearing children and acquiring the food to sustain them. Such reasons may show as much moral sensitivity as a desire to raise ten children. Hence the family, long before the disaster-point, decided to limit its size.

Any society, including the whole human society, may reason similarly. Starvation is not the only urgent reason for limiting population. Long before people have to go hungry, a society may see that quality of life is more important than the number of people and that expansion of population threatens values as humanly important as survival. The availability of raw materials to sustain civilized life, the psychological problems of crowding, and the provision of educational opportunities are all factors in the population explosion.

Furthermore, man has acquired rather little understanding of the complex and delicate ecology that sustains him. His ambitious efforts to solve some problems unwittingly produce others. The Aswan dam, for example, is a colossal effort to increase the agricultural productivity and the electric power available to Egypt. But, even apart from the grim fact that its calculated gains will barely provide for the increase in population during its construction, it has yet unknown effects on the farm productivity and the marine life in the Nile delta, including even in early stages a major blow to the sardine industry.[8] Any ecologist can tell dozens of stories of well-intentioned efforts to increase productivity or destroy rapacious insects that succeeded in their aim, but backfired with harmful effects for nature and society.

In the United States the "death" of Lake Erie and the occasional smog crises in cities are portents of potentially far worse disasters. The fact of the matter is that we simply do not know how much exhaust wastes from airplanes or how much denuding of forests this planet can stand. At some point an increase in the earth's temperature can start an irreversible melting of polar icecaps that will change the contours of continents. At some point the saturation of the atmosphere with excessive carbon dioxide (to say nothing of poisonous carbon monoxide) can shift markedly the prospects for human life on the earth. In the gradual increases of such processes, there are probably thresholds, now unknown, at which the danger becomes critical and irrevocable.

Christian theology is not committed to a blind reverence of nature or to the notion that nature handles all things for the best. Man has the right and the power to modify nature. But reckless intrusions into nature combine religious arrogance with practical destruction.

With this point the population problem shifts its terms. So long as hunger alone is the issue, population is a problem for the economically poor nations, not for the rich. But in ecological terms it is greatest in the most affluent nations. The affluent American consumes and produces wastes on a vast scale. Former Senator Ernest Gruening, probably the most expert of all members of Congress on this subject, has said: "The average American consumes in natural resources as much as do thirty residents of India."[9] The Harvard nutritionist Jean Mayer writes: "The ecology of the earth—its streams, woods, animals—can accommodate itself better to a rising *poor* population than to a rising *rich* population. Indeed, to save the ecology, the population will have to decrease as the disposable income increases."[10]

Seen in this light, the United States is in the midst of a population crisis. With its embarrassing agricultural surpluses, it can feed many more people. But it lives and breeds at the cost of the devastation of its natural environment. DDT has inflicted great harm on nature, and no one yet knows how much harm it has done or can do to mankind. We know something about the pollution of the atmosphere by industry and jet planes, about the fouling of fresh waters with human and industrial wastes, about the scarring of the landscape by automobiles insatiably greedy for more highways, about mountains of abandoned cars, about cities desperately searching for places to dump their wastes. We know something, too, about the inadequacies of hospitals, of educational institutions, of recreational opportunities.

Not all these problems can be blamed on population alone. A people with a different sense of ethical and aesthetic priorities could handle prosperity with more respect for nature and humanity. Urgent necessity may sooner or later require technology to do more about its own devastation—for example, produce a practical electric or steam automobile to replace the noxious internal combustion engine. But it is equally true that people who write and read books like this—people who consider themselves ethically sensitive—are large-scale consumers. We, more than the poor people in urban ghettoes and on subsistence farms, are responsible for turning forests into paper, for using electrical energy, for keeping the airlines crowded with poison-emitting planes. And if we accomplish some of our nobler aims of eliminating poverty and increasing education, we will make more people able and eager to consume on the big scale.

For such reasons, many students of population judge that the people of the United States would be wise to stabilize their population now and that it is as important in the United States as anywhere in the world to aim for the goal of an average 2.2 children per family, the number needed to maintain equilibrium. Certainly the people of this country have no right to think condescendingly about population problems as the sole worry of the inhabitants of Asia and Latin America.

III. Why People Procreate

People procreate, for the most part, because they want to. Of all acts of human creativity, the bringing to birth of another person, clearly kin and successor to two parents, yet a unique person within the entire human race, is the most remarkable. There are, of course, many foolish and perverse reasons why people crave offspring; often they mistreat their children by regarding them as extensions of the parents and agents of the parents' unrealized expectations. But human love and creativity are closely related. Most parents want children and want to love them. Furthermore, the act of conception is a peculiarly appropriate outcome of the act of sexual love. As Soren Kierkegaard, the crusty but sensitive bachelor, put it, to marry for the sake of begetting children is an insult to the bride and a degradation of love; nevertheless, children are a blessing upon marriage.

Sometimes, of course, people procreate unintentionally. They choose sex, and procreation follows. The awareness of pregnancy may be a surprise, even a bitter surprise. The problem of the unintended child—who may be unwanted and resented, or may be wanted but not quite intended—is a serious one for the child, for parents, and for the total world with its expanding population.

Mankind is fairly on the way to solving this problem, at least in principle. Contraception enlarges the realm of intentionality and reduces the realm of accident. For the most part, this movement is an ethical gain, comparable to the other areas in which human intentionality has gained ground over accident or fate. A theological warning may be in order here. Christians have always regarded an infant as a gracious divine gift, not simply the result of their contriving. But to be able to say "no" or "not just now" to a gift need not detract from its glory when it is wanted and acclaimed. Nor need it destroy the spontaneity that is part of the Christian ethic at its best. The gift will himself (or herself) give emphatic evidence of spontaneity, and the availability of contraceptives to the parents will actually increase the possibilities of spontaneity in conjugal love.

I have said that man is on the way to solving the problem of the unwanted child, because the problem is not yet solved. For the purposes of this chapter, it is not necessary to go into the profound personal questions of the difference between "wanted" and "unwanted," in view of the ambivalence of many human desires and feelings. Those questions may never be entirely answered or even answerable. But using "wanted" and "unwanted" in the simplest sense, the question then becomes one of the availability of effective contraception. Medical science has made immense progress in recent years by inventing contraceptives that are adequate for many people. The news about them has spread widely, although still not universally. They are increasingly available. And, as I have indicated earlier, they are morally acceptable and desirable to an increasing number of people.

But the search continues for the "ideal" contraceptive. Such a contraceptive would be 100 percent effective, usable without destroying the spontaneity of sexual love, cheap enough to be made available widely in the most impoverished societies, free from undesirable side effects, simple enough for unsophisticated and illiterate people to employ. It would have one other important quality: It would so work as to require a definite, intentional act in order to attain conception rather than to prevent it. Such a contraceptive may be on the way. Experiments may be leading to an injection, something like the shots people take to prevent diseases, that would make a man or woman sterile for a predictable period of time, say a year, but that would be revocable by another injection. If the experiments succeed, the problem of the unwanted child will be solved, at least for all parents who gain access to the contraceptive and are willing to use it. The actual attainment of such a contraceptive is a problem of technique, not of ethics.

The ideal contraceptive, if attained, will have ethical reverberations. It will make possible uninhibited sexual relations without fear of unwanted pregnancies. To the extent that such fear has been a motive and sanction for sexual morality, old restraints, already weakened, will crumble. This possibility is, to some people, frightening. But, to a considerable extent, society and the churches appear to be ready to accept it. The Christian sexual ethic, in its Biblical if not in all its cultural forms, did not in any case rest upon the sanction and threat of unwanted pregnancy. Christians may find that the lifting of the sanction enables them to see more profoundly than before the meaning of fidelity. If not, they will have to think through again the meaning of sex and its responsible expression. That is the subject for another inquiry; here the issue is population. There is no doubt that the development of the ideal contraceptive would become a major factor in dampening the population explosion, and further research in that area is a contribution to the problem. Meanwhile, the increased information about and availability of contraceptives are a major help.

However, many discussions of population settle too quickly on contraception as the key to the solution. The fact is that many of the people who are crowding the earth's surface today, not least in the areas where hunger is greatest, were wanted and intended by their parents. Furthermore, many factors apart from contraception influence the frequency of procreation. Hence, specialists concerned about population are increasingly talking about "the crisis of the wanted child."[11] Here we are no longer waiting for technical developments; we are concerned with immediate human desires and apprehensions.

There is considerable evidence that, roughly speaking, people have about as many children as social influences and personal desire lead them to want. Anybody knows exceptions to such a generalization, but in broad terms it sums up some relevant data. Dr. André E. Hellegers has pointed out that in the United States the "average achieved fertility of the white family" in 1800 was 7.0 children, a figure that dropped to about 2.0 in the 1930's, then rose to about 4.0 in the post World War II baby boom. Of course, contraceptives were available in the 1930's, when demographers were worried about a decline in population, but neither the intrauterine device (IUD) nor the pill—the methods that many enthusiasts for birth control pin their hopes upon—had been introduced. Still more to the point, Dr. Hellegers calls attention to the fact that in France and Switzerland the shift from large to small families took place "in the early nineteenth century even before the vulcanization of rubber."[12] Clearly, population growth is not an inverse function of handy contraceptives.

Nor, contrary to much popular mythology, can rates of reproduction be correlated with any precision to religious belief. The anti-contraceptive ethic of Roman Catholicism makes some difference in some places, but the data confound the expectations both of those devout clerics who think it should make a difference and of the anti-clericals who want to blame Catholicism for preventing restraint. A recent analysis points out that "the historic transition from large to small families in the West began in two Roman Catholic nations—France and Ireland."[13] France, despite both governmental and ecclesiastical pressures to the contrary, led all Europe in the decline in birth rate. Not until the 1920's did famous (or infamous) Sweden and England catch up. In Europe today the birth rates in predominantly Catholic countries are practically indistinguishable from those in other countries.[14] Roman Catholic Latin America, of course, has a high birth rate, as do parts of non-Catholic Asia and Africa; but one study of Latin America indicates that women who attend Mass frequently have slightly fewer children than merely nominal Catholics.[15]

If neither availability of contraceptives nor religious belief can be correlated closely with high birth rates, three other factors come somewhat closer to establishing a correlation: education, economic development, and high mortality among children. All countries with adult illiteracy of above 50 percent have annual birth rates of above thirty-five per thousand people.[16] These countries are also the economically underdeveloped countries; birth rates in developed countries range from thirteen to thirty.[17]

Infant and childhood mortality is a special case. Obviously one side of the story is that high mortality cancels out high birth rates. Over past centuries it was the high death rate that prevented a population explosion; the new factor in modern times is far less the increase in births than the postponement of deaths. But the other side of the story is that high childhood mortality means that parents want to have enough children so that some will survive to adulthood. In many a society the economic security of aged parents depends upon their sons. The family system of social security leads the parents to want enough male offspring that some will certainly survive to adulthood. Rather suddenly in recent years many societies have greatly reduced the fatal effects of some diseases—above all, malaria. Hence, far more children survive and procreate, thus expanding the population. But parents have not yet broken old habits and revised their expectations to take account of the new situation. Furthermore, the parent is not going to change his desires because of a statistical probability that holds for the entire society; he wants assurance that in his specific family he will have survivors, especially male survivors. Thus Roger Revelle, of the Center for Population Studies at Harvard University, concludes: "We are faced with the paradox that only by reducing infant and child mortality, perhaps down to the levels existing in the Western world, will the conditions be produced which may encourage people in the less developed countries to limit the size of their families to sufficiently small numbers."[18] Obviously, economic change, making aged parents less dependent upon their sons, will help also, although the reasons why people want survivors are generally more than economic.

It appears then that improved education, economic development, and enhanced health give the best possibilities of leading people to desire small families. Happily, these three aims embody important human values. Crusades that center on population alone are likely to seem almost ruthless in their single-mindedness. A barrage of propaganda, persuading people that fewer of them should have been born, is likely to seem dehumanizing. None of us likes the implication that the world would be better off without us. But social changes that enhance the value of life are likely to increase people's self-respect and their appreciation of others, even while leading parents to prefer small families, also for humanistic reasons. Within such a context contraception is a great advantage. I have already argued that people who want small families are likely to have small families, even without contraceptives, whereas even the best contraceptives will not prevent conception among people who want big families. But for those who are ready to limit conception, contraceptives increase the efficiency of intentions. Also, in contrast to the rigorous methods of delayed marriage, sexual abstention within marriage, and abortion, they contribute to human sensitivity and the joy of the family relationship.

Thus far the argument is hopeful but incomplete. It is hopeful because it holds that an emphasis on certain humanly desirable goals—education, economic development, and health—will eventually lead deprived societies, as it has already led the affluent industrial societies, to restraint in reproduction. It is incomplete because it does not take sufficient account of the urgency of swift action and of the need (mentioned in Part II of this chapter) for the affluent societies, including the most affluent society of all, to come to terms with the issue.

It is not enough to hope that the same processes that slowed population growth in industrial societies will eventually do the same in the less developed societies. The marked decline in birth rates in Western Europe took place chiefly between 1880 and 1960 (except for France, where it started in 1820). If India and Latin America should play out a comparable scenario over 80 years, the result will be untold suffering. The process, including the changing of age-old beliefs and mores, must be speeded.

Also, it is not enough to hint that the developing countries might follow the example of the affluent societies, when the latter expand more slowly but still too fast for social equilibrium and ecology. Somehow nations like the United States must also get the message.

The necessity and urgency of the task, in the United States and around the world, require investigation of programs that actually might be undertaken.

IV. The Possibilities of Purposive Social Action

Many methods of controlling population growth are not humanly acceptable. For example, a wholesale slaughter of infants is technically possible, but is morally as bad as any evil it might be designed to prevent. Some people would say that any interference with the right to procreate is wrong. But in any society the human acceptability of severe acts depends in part upon the intensity of the crisis that prompts the acts. In times of war and riot people accept infringements of their freedom that they reject at other times. The programs that any society will accept for limitation of population depend to a considerable extent upon that society's perception of the danger of population growth.

In considering the social acceptability of various possible procedures, I do not make the assumption that such acceptability is the final ethical authority. Any humanistic ethic, and certainly any theological ethic, must recognize that social acceptability is sometimes a flimsy criterion for integrity and that one of the assets of any society is its prophets who challenge socially acceptable behavior. Even so, policy decisions must take account of the social acceptability of alternative possibilities for action. And even the most transcendent ethic must, when it enters into public policy, take account of the way in which the actual pressures of historical life determine what men at their best can do and what in their necessity they are willing to do. The extent of the threat will determine the rigor, possibly even the ruthlessness, with which men will move to meet it.

Today the most skilled professional estimates of the danger move between wide extremes. There is universal agreement that continuation of the population explosion means havoc. The uncertainty concerns the likelihood of bringing population under control.

Dr. Paul Ehrlich, the Stanford biologist, speaks with powerful impact of the grimmest possibilities. "The battle to feed all of humanity is over. In the 1970's the world will undergo famines—hundreds of millions of people are going to starve to death in spite of any crash programs embarked upon now."[19] The most spectacular programs to increase food production can only achieve "a stay of execution," apart from drastic measures to control population; and, at best, large-scale starvation is inevitable. Among several of his imaginary scenarios of the future, the worst include social chaos leading to nuclear destruction and the best suggests starvation of a fifth of the world's population before adoption of a successful program to bring stability.[20]

Dr. Donald J. Bogue, University of Chicago sociologist, speaks for the optimistic minority among specialists. "In fact, it is quite reasonable to assume that *the world population crisis is a phenomenon of the twentieth century, and will be largely if not entirely a matter of history when humanity moves into the twenty-first century.* . . . It is probable that by the year 2000 each of the major world regions will have a population growth rate that is either zero or is easily within the capacity of its expanding economy to support."[21] This estimate depends upon a projection, not of the general trends of recent decades, but of the "switch-over" that has taken place in a few areas since about 1965. Dr. Bogue expects the "contraception adoption explosion," now beginning, to make a measurable difference soon. He acknowledges that he has not persuaded his professional colleagues. "Most were angry," he says. "I found no one who agreed with me."[22]

At first inspection these two forecasts appear to be about as far apart as any two forecasts could be, and they may shake all faith in expert testimony. Closer analysis shows areas of agreement. Both agree that years of painful crisis lie ahead for immense human societies. Both agree on the necessity for immense efforts to prevent starvation and curtail the expansion of population. Ehrlich's reason for publicizing his dire forebodings is to jolt people into strenuous action; Bogue's reason for hope is that such action is beginning to "pay off" and that continued research and action will accomplish even more. Even so, the difference between the two forecasts has an important consequence for one major ethical and social issue: the exercise of freedom and compulsion in restraining population growth. If Bogue's estimates are right, the human race is on the way to solving this problem through the exercise of rational freedom. If Ehrlich's predictions are correct, social pressures and even forms of coercion will become necessary.

Freedom and compulsion never exist as total processes in isolation from each other. But, to get at the issue, it is easy to suggest two imaginary and abstract possibilities, neither of which will actually be carried out. The first aims to maximize freedom. It lets parents decide the number of their offspring, freed from any political or economic pressures. It provides families with a maximum of information and a selection of contraceptive agents to use as they decide. It assures them of adequate housing and income for the size family of their choice. They are thus freed to make their reasoned decision solely on the basis of their wishes, influenced to whatever extent they choose by a sense of responsibility to the good of the society. Today a few societies approach this plan, without going so far as to remove the economic pressures that operate on most families.

The second plan takes more account of the social dangers of uninhibited reproduction and resorts to direct coercion to restrict births. It sets a limit—perhaps one child per mother in critically overpopulated areas, perhaps two or three children per mother elsewhere—and enforces it. Technically the plan is quite feasible, at least in societies where children are born in hospitals. The obstetrician who delivers the baby can tie the mother's tubes so as to prevent further conception. (The reason for concentrating on women is not male bias. It is simply that it is fairly obvious how many children a woman has born, less obvious how many a man has fathered; it is also easy to locate women at the time of childbirth.) No society actually uses such a plan, and its encroachment on personal freedom would cause great resistance in any society. But a society driven to desperation by food shortages might conceivably reason that this kind of compulsion is as humane as is a *laissez-faire* policy of "let them be born and starve."

The point in suggesting two unrealistic plans is simply to show that neither freedom nor compulsion in a complete and abstract form is a social possibility. Life is always a mixture of the two. Starvation is the most obvious form of compulsion that is presently reducing population. Economic pressures are a more moderate, but still real, form of compulsion. Most societies, our own in particular, resent economic pressure less than political pressure, because of an assumption that economic pressure is part of the nature of life whereas political pressure is contrived. That assumption is not entirely accurate, because the distribution of economic pressure is always the result (at least in part) of political contrivance. Since some compulsion and pressure are part of life, there is nothing inherently unethical about social programs that seek to take account of and to rationalize pressure.

Men, in their craving for freedom and their concern for human dignity, will seek to meet the population crisis with a minimum of coercion. I fully share this desire. In testimony before a Senate committee in 1966, endorsing legislation to facilitate family planning, I based my advocacy upon three values: freedom, peace, and the dignity of man. Here I repeat part of that testimony concerning freedom:

> In the United States a majority of families practice some sort of planning of procreation. Their children are wanted, not the result of fate or accident. People are free to choose methods of planning in accordance with their consciences and their desires. But this freedom is at present denied to some, due to ignorance or poverty. . . .
>
> The same pattern prevails on a world scale. . . . If we are concerned for mankind, we cannot deny to them the freedom so widely practiced in this country.
>
> Today the opportunity for family planning, in accord-

> ance with the personal beliefs and purposes of parents, is a right available to part of the human race. The same right is closed to many because of poverty, ignorance, and geography. Justice demands that this human right be opened to all.[23]

The reason for recording that statement here is to indicate my strong disposition toward freedom and my reluctance to resort to coercion. Simultaneously I must repeat that sheer freedom, detached from social responsibility and the elements of coercion inherent in social living, is an inconceivable abstraction. Hence, any ethical inquiry must ask whether there are points at which society is justified in imposing limitations upon procreation for the sake of those living and those yet to be born. The possibility cannot be ruled out *a priori.*

Any freedom within a society is related to some coercion. The freedom of public safety is related to coercive prohibitions of crime. Free public education depends upon coercive taxes. Free public parks require some (presently inadequate) restraints upon pollution and destruction of land, air, water, and vegetation. Professor Garrett Hardin of the University of California at Santa Barbara makes a case that is at least arguable when he states: "To couple the concept of freedom to breed with the belief that everyone born has an equal right to the commons [i.e., to food and other resources of the world] is to lock the world into a tragic course of action."[24] Paul Ehrlich is ready to commend coercion in a good cause, and he wonders why people are quite willing to fight coercive wars, yet wince at coercion in population policy.[25]

Actually the alternatives are not total freedom or coercion. A spectrum of possibilities is available: uninhibited freedom, rational persuasion, social pressures, economic pressures, manipulative devices, coercion. A society usually settles for something between the extremes. People can live with pressures that leave them room for maneuver. Yet just this possibility of manipulation that is not quite coercion, especially when practiced with the sophisticated guile of psychological and social sciences, opens one of the most insidious of realms. Kenneth Boulding, distinguished economist and social analyst, writes: "It is a slightly nightmarish thought that social science may be even more damning to mankind than physical science. Physical science merely culminates in the pain and death of the body under the bomb; social science may culminate in the damnation of the soul in the manipulative society."[26]

Such a statement makes it all the more significant when Boulding himself suggests a plan for regulation of population. Society, or its social planners, could set the rate of reproduction necessary to maintain a stable population (usually 2.2). Then it could issue to women licenses, not entirely unlike trading stamps. Ten units (called deci-childs) might authorize one birth. Each young woman could be issued 22 units. These could be bought, sold, inherited, or given as gifts. The operation of the market would determine the price. The number of children permissible to any family would depend in part upon its desires, its priorities, and its economic abilities, while the total rate of reproduction would be controlled.[27]

Boulding combines a sensitive Quaker conscience, a sharp wit, and skill in the social sciences and game theory. It is impossible to read his proposal without assuming that he has his tongue a little way in his cheek; but it is also impossible to read Boulding's tongue-in-cheek proposals without assuming that he has some serious purpose behind them. In this case the scientist who is an incisive critic of manipulation is simultaneously showing the necessity of some kind of social control even when he is revealing its moral offensiveness.

Bernard Berelson, president of the Population Council, has made a nearly exhaustive catalogue of possible policies for meeting the crisis of population.[28] In addition to voluntary measures and to augmented research, which are now endorsed by almost everyone, he catalogues a number of proposals involving some degree of pressure. The following list is a selection from his compilation, chosen without regard to his ordering solely for the purpose of indicating some of the varieties of coercion-pressure-persuasion that have been proposed in various parts of the world:

Involuntary restraints:

- Addition to the water supply of temporary sterilants or of fertility-reducing agents (yet to be discovered);
- Compulsory injections of time-capsule contraceptives, reversible under strict social controls;
- Kenneth Boulding's proposal (described above).

Financial inducements:

- Direct payments to people who undergo sterilization or practice effective contraception;
- Reversal of tax systems to favor small families, or limitations of government benefits (education, medical treatment, housing) to favor small families;
- Pensions for poor parents with few children.

Revised institutional structures:

- Delayed marriage (either compulsory or financially advantageous);
- Restructuring of the family to make the present normal expectation (permanent marriage with children) only one option among others.

Some of the foregoing proposals are not yet technically feasible, but scientific developments may make them possible. Some would allow for cheating; but a determined society could impose fairly strict enforcement by requiring abortions of all pregnancies outside the rules.

Anybody inspecting this list is likely to spot plans which

he regards as politically impossible or morally abhorrent. But available alternatives sometimes determine moral decisions. Men in desperation—war is the obvious example—do things that in better circumstances they would call immoral. The responsibility of the moral agent is not simply to oppose evil; it is to contribute to the formation of a society in which men do not face only evil choices.

Almost anyone would agree that the prospect of an increasingly polluted planet, or even neighborhood, justifies *some* inhibitions on freedom. The prospect—and the present fact—of starvation justifies *some* compulsion. A function of social ethics is to design inhibitions and compulsions that interfere as little as possible with human dignity and integrity.

That brings the issue back to the starting point of this chapter. If men were not human, not creatures of dignity and freedom, the managers of society might simply select the most efficient restraint upon population and enforce it. But in dealing with people it is important to place the technical issue in a human context. The temptation is to take short cuts that destroy the human dignity that might make voluntary answers possible. But imposed decisions are likely to meet resistance; decisions that people make themselves are more likely to be effective. Robert C. Cook, president of the Population Reference Bureau, has pointed out that in the several countries that have achieved an approximate balance of births and deaths, there has been no legislation to that end, and there has sometimes been legislation aimed at keeping a high birth rate.[29] Philip M. Hauser, director of the University of Chicago Population Research and Training Center, has made the same point emphatically: "The fact is that decreases in fertility in what are now the economically advanced nations were achieved completely on a voluntary basis."[30]

Hence we may hope with Donald Bogue that education

is already beginning a "contraceptive adoption explosion." We may hope with Roger Revelle that reduced infant and child mortality and a higher standard of living will moderate parents' desires for large families and, when joined with available contraceptives, will ameliorate the problem. But hopes are not enough. And idealism that neglects the actual context of decision in its exaltation of freedom is not enough. The sober fact is that the human race is *not* free to procreate without limit. That fact must be brought home to people. Political devices that confront people with the authentic limits upon freedom, rather than imposing artificial restraints upon them, are justified. Political ingenuity has the task of recognizing the distinction between the two methods and working out the meaning of the first.

Societies change ethical attitudes and habits in complex and subtle ways. Rational persuasion is part of the process. Confrontation with hard fact is also part of it. A changed personal and social self-image, a modified conceptualization and symbolization of the world, are other parts. And the parts are mixed up with each other. Out of the present situation revised sensitivities and practices, not all predictable, can be expected. Some day the "mother of the year" may be invariably the mother of only two children. The large family, even when well reared and educated, may be considered a symbol of social irresponsibility. The recklessly breeding father may be considered not the virile hale fellow well met, but something of a buffoon or a menace. Some feelings will get hurt in the process of change, but people are getting hurt now. Whether the change can come in time to prevent far more terrible hurts than the world now experiences, we do not yet know. Haste is urgent. Technical advances will help, but purposive action, sensitive to human values, will be equally important. Man has demonstrated frequently in recent years a capacity to change ways of living deeply imbedded in memory and history—

sometimes for better, sometimes for worse. He had better change his habits of procreation swiftly.

One sign of the integrity of a person or group is willingness to live by the restraints expected of others. That willingness is suddenly becoming important in respect to population. People in impoverished areas of the world sometimes resent propaganda for birth control as the desire of wealthy nations for genocide among the poor nations. Residents of ghettoes sometimes dismiss the same propaganda as racism in dominant whites. It would help if the propaganda could be accompanied with the message, perhaps unspoken, "We suggest nothing to you that we are not doing ourselves."

At present the affluent white subculture in the United States, from which come many of the pleas for birth control, can honestly claim to practice family planning. It cannot yet claim to be aware of the dimensions of the problem or to be seriously concerned to stabilize population. Its birth rates are lower than those of less affluent cultures and subcultures, but it is still expanding at a portentous rate. It is not enough to answer that it has accepted the discipline of living within its means—even when that answer is in some senses accurate. It is this subculture that in its consumption and its destruction of the environment with its wastes outdoes all others. What it could once do cheerfully, even with innocent conscience, it can do no more.

Population control will not solve all or even very many of the world's urgent problems. But without it all the other problems are becoming insoluble. Ecology successfully restrains other species than man. Natural enemies hold the species in check, and if it gets out of hand and destroys its food supplies, it diminishes in numbers. Man thus far has been spectacularly successful, despite costly mistakes and human suffering, in outwitting the ecological system. But his ominous increase in numbers, coupled with his ravenous consumption, can easily lead him to destruction. He knows something of the reality and threat of mass starvation. He senses the destructiveness of war. He barely guesses what may happen if he raises the temperature of the earth a few degrees or shifts seriously the balance between oxygen and carbon dioxide. He is engaged in a costly roulette game, gambling on his own survival, without knowing the odds.

Astronaut Colonel Frank Borman, asked how the earth looked from the heavens, answered, "I thought: How small, how fragile, how beautiful."[31] Because of man's unique gifts among all creatures, he has become—to a notable degree—custodian of this small, fragile, beautiful home and the living beings who inhabit it. The greatest predator of all creatures, he is suddenly learning that his privilege is his burden.

Contemporary Christians often echo Dietrich Bonhoeffer's statement that man has come of age. To move from adolescence to adulthood is to assume new powers, joined to new responsibilities. Procreation is a gift, not an invention of man. The control of it is now in his power, and it has become his responsibility.

NOTES

1. The figure of 10,000 per day is the generally accepted estimate of governmental and other specialists. It was used by President Richard Nixon in his message to Congress on the population problem in 1969. The text is in *The New York Times*, July 19, 1969.

2. Ivan L. Bennett, Jr., M.D., "Meeting World Food Needs," *Sais Review* (School of Advanced International Studies of the Johns Hopkins University), Vol. 13, No. 3 (Spring, 1969), p. 9.

3. John Nuveen, "The Facts of Life," in *Family Planning in an Exploding Population,* edited by John A. O'Brien (New York: Hawthorn Books, Inc., 1968), p. 35.

4. Paul R. Ehrlich, *The Population Bomb* (New York: Ballantine

Books, 1968), p. 20. The estimate is from the British physicist, J. H. Fremlin.

5. See, for example, *Contraception and Holiness,* a symposium with introduction by Archbishop Thomas D. Roberts, S. J. (New York: Herder and Herder, 1964). See also John T. Noonan, Jr., *Contraception* (New York: Mentor-Omega, 1965).

6. John A. O'Brien, "Birth Control and the Catholic Conscience," *Reader's Digest,* January, 1969, p. 3.

7. *Ibid.,* pp. 2–6.

8. See *Newsweek,* July 7, 1969.

9. Senator Ernest Gruening, *Population Crisis,* Part I, 1966, Hearings before the Subcommittee on Foreign Aid Expenditures of the Committee on Government Operations, United States Senate, on S. 1676 (Washington: U.S. Government Printing Office, 1966), p. 11.

10. Jean Mayer, "Toward a Non-Malthusian Population Policy," *Columbia Forum,* Vol. 12, No. 2 (Summer, 1969), p. 13. Dr. Mayer is professor of nutrition at Harvard and a consultant to United Nations organizations. He differs from many authorities in thinking that the world food situation is actually improving slightly and can continue to improve; but he argues that population control is absolutely essential for human and ecological reasons.

11. The phrase, "the crisis of the wanted child," is the subject of a memorandum to the professional staff of Planned Parenthood-World Population by Frederick S. Jaffe, Vice President for Program Planning and Development, January 18, 1968.

12. André E. Hellegers, M.D., "Factors and Correctives in Population Expansion," *Sais Review,* Vol. 13, No. 3 (Spring, 1969), p. 24.

13. *Population Profile* (Washington: Population Reference Bureau, Inc.), July, 1969, p. 4.

14. *Ibid.,* pp. 4–5.

15. *Ibid.,* p. 5. The study was made by the United Nations Latin American Demographic Center (CELADE) and Cornell University.

16. André E. Hellegers, M.D., *op. cit.,* p. 25.

17. Roger Revelle, preparatory paper on "Technology and the World Population-Hunger Problem" for National Consultation on Technology and Human Values, convened by the National Council of Churches, Chicago, May 2–4, 1967, p. 5. Dr. Revelle is Director of the Center for Population Studies at Harvard University.

18. *Ibid.*, p. 11. Much of the reasoning in this paragraph is borrowed from Revelle.

19. Paul R. Ehrlich, *op. cit.*, p. 11.

20. *Ibid.*, pp. 72–80.

21. Donald J. Bogue, "The End of the Population Explosion," *The Public Interest,* No. 7 (Spring, 1967), pp. 11–20. The italics are in the original. Dr. Bogue is professor of sociology and director of the Community and Family Center, University of Chicago. Another hopeful analysis is made by Frank W. Notestein, "The Population Crisis: Reasons for Hope," *Foreign Affairs,* October, 1967, pp. 167–180.

22. Donald J. Bogue, quoted by David Lyle, "The Human Race Has, Maybe, Thirty-Five Years left," reprinted from *Esquire,* Sept. 1967, by Planned Parenthood-World Population.

23. Roger L. Shinn, *Population Crisis,* Part I, 1966, Hearings Before the Subcommittee on Foreign Aid Expenditures of the Committee on Government Operations, United States Senate, on S. 1676 (Washington: U.S. Government Printing Office, 1966), pp. 171–176.

24. Garrett Hardin, "The Tragedy of the Commons," *Science,* Vol. 152 (December 13, 1968), pp. 1243–1248.

25. Paul R. Ehrlich, *op. cit.,* p. 166.

26. Kenneth Boulding, *The Organizational Revolution* (New York: Harper and Row, 1953), p. 220.

27. Kenneth Boulding, *The Meaning of the Twentieth Century* (New York: Harper & Row, 1964), pp. 135–136.

28. Bernard Berelson, "Beyond Family Planning," *Science,* Vol. 163 (February 7, 1969), pp. 533–543.

29. Robert C. Cook, *Population Crisis,* Part I, 1966, *op. cit.*, p. 565.

30. Philip M. Hauser, *Population Crisis,* Part 2, 1967–68 (Washington: U.S. Government Printing Office, 1968), p. 492.

31. Col. Frank Borman, interview in Madrid, reported in *The New York Times,* February 18, 1969.

CONSERVATION

MAN'S PLACE IN NATURE IN RECENT WESTERN THOUGHT

by Professor Clarence J. Glacken

I

An outstanding characteristic of contemporary living is our preoccupation with the effect of present civilization on the natural environment, whether it be the survival of a bay, an Alpine wild flower, or an African rhinoceros. This observation, so banal that it takes courage to make it, may be placed in perspective by adding that it has been an outstanding characteristic for an exceedingly minute period of human history. In the first edition of his *Principles of Geology* (1830–33), Charles Lyell said that man, like water, wind, frost, plants, and animals, was an agent in changing the face of the earth; the age of man's influence, however, had just begun. Now, less than 140 years later, the preoccupation with man's influence, ranging from the effects of millions of internal combustion engines in a city like Los Angeles to various African tribal laws and customs on the use of fire, is worldwide.

A second outstanding fact is that many of these contemporary observations lead to pessimistic conclusions. This is an even more recent development. The first comprehensive and sustained work on the nature of man's modifications of the earth was George P. Marsh's *Man and Nature* (1864). Today this pessimism and the literature it is producing are based on such obvious problems as world population increase, largely in the form of increases in population densities and the evils they bring, pollution, threatened extinction of many plant and animal species; environmental destruction in traditional societies; speculative land development in the so-called civilized societies—none of them requires learned volumes of history for their elucidation.

A third outstanding fact is that these modifications of the natural world by man have been poorly integrated into either the history or the philosophy of civilization. We might here make exceptions of works written around the theme of man's increasing control over nature, but these often have a strong optimistic, technological bias, as if all changes were purposive, for the better, and made strictly in accordance with a plan for world progress which civilization and its dutiful burghers were carrying out.

Today we have nothing like the dominating cohesive ideas of the past, a past so recent in time, so remote in philosophy. The argument of design in nature, the idea of history as a continuing unfolding of God's will, various monisms like environmental determinism, the idea of progress, seem remote and foreign among present-day realities. Faith in science and especially in technology (granting they are not easily separated) has in large part replaced them, but there are many dissenting voices. Only recently has the dogma that science should press forward with its discoveries, regardless of where they might lead, been questioned. Faith in science, faith in technology, are far less persuasive in our day than the design argument in the eighteenth century and the idea of progress in Victorian England.

II

In this paper it is not so much with the facts of a world changed by man that I am concerned as with the various interpretations made of them. I wish to select a few of those which have been made, roughly since the end of the eighteenth century, without any pretense of exhausting the opportunities or insisting that the ones I have chosen are the best examples, although the trends they represent I think are correct. Historically, they have grown in part out of attempted answers to the question: Is man a significant force in modifying the surface of the earth?

Basic to this literature is its strong anthropocentrism. With the decline of religious faith and of the idea of God's care for the world, a similar decline in the power of secular teleologies like the idea of progress, and the growth in influence of existential ideas, there has come to be, of necessity, more and more reliance on human-engendered values. These values are necessary for survival; they are based on a belief that for life to have meaning, it must have links with the past and with posterity. The same belief that is the basis of the traditional Chinese family system is also the philosophical basis of much of the literature on the wise use of the natural environment. It is this belief in historical continuity and the values it enshrines that also inspires movements for the preservation of man's creations like the Parthenon and natural phenomena like the redwoods. Few want and few could tolerate a disembodied present.

During the last century and a half, certainly since Hume and Kant, the trend has been in the direction of saying that it is we who bestow value and beauty to nature, and since Buffon's time a second trend, of uncertain course, it is true, has been toward a conception of man as an "ecological dominant," to use Carl Sauer's expression. In this view, the environment can no longer be understood without reference to man and his activities. In *La Vision du passé,* Teilhard de Chardin makes the suggestive remark that a century ago man thought of himself as a simple observer, after Darwin as a simple branch of evolution, while now he is beginning to see that the principal trunk of the tree of life passes through him.[1] In fact, in recent years, there has been more and more emphasis on the role of man as a directive force not only on his own but on the evolution of other forms of life.

III

Before the end of the eighteenth century, certain ideas about man as a modifier of the natural world were well established.[2] Perhaps the most important was the idea that man, as the self-judged and self-appointed highest form of the creation, has a natural lordship over the rest of the world. To most human beings, I suppose, this has seemed a reasonable position! This idea existed in classical and Judaeo-Christian versions, the latter often incorporating elements of the former. In the classical form, seen most comprehensively in the Stoic philosophy, man is master of the creation because of unique endowments. He is a being uniquely qualified not only to observe, worship, and understand the natural world but also to participate in it and to change it. The mind, the hand, the eye, erect carriage are elements of man's unique endowment which allow him, unlike other forms of life, to arrange and order creation. This distinction between "human" and "brute" action has been one of the key ideas in the history of Western civilization, at least in that body of thought concerned with man's place in nature and his relation to other forms of life. The puzzles inherent in this problem have been important to such disparate thinkers as Aristotle, Cicero, Buffon, Marsh, T.H. Huxley, and Albert Schweitzer. They are an outgrowth of study and speculation about the differences among life forms and the nature of the gulf between human and other forms of life. In Western thought, a strong tradition asserts the reality of the gulf. In a famous passage in the *Nichomachean Ethics,* Aristotle said that the activity of God "is the activity of contemplation." Those human activities most akin to the divine activity of contemplation will be the greatest source of happiness. Lower animals "cannot partake of happiness because they are completely devoid of the contemplative activity."[3] At least 2,200 years later, T.H. Huxley in his famous essay *Man's Place in Nature* (1863) insisted that, while all life had a common origin, man had evolved to an exalted and unique place in nature, and that the gulf should be a source of pride.

In the Judaeo-Christian tradition, the most obvious evidences are the Genesis passages and others, especially in Psalms 8 and 104, in which man is given dominion over the rest of the creation because he has been made in the image of God and because God has participated directly in his creation. Adam had the power of naming animals, and Noah seemingly had no trouble in organizing the whole animal creation before embarking. Even in classical times, however, man could attain this role without religious credentials. In Lucretius' poem, one role of man is that of a controller of plant and animal life—without him brambles and wild beasts alike would mutiply in chaotic profusion. This idea suggests another, within or without a religious setting, the idea of man as a steward of the creation, implying care, cosseting, superintendence, and responsibility to the unborn. The pre-evolutionary theories of continuities in creation such as the idea of a great chain of being, when they were not narrowly anthropocentric (when it was admitted that man's high place in nature did not mean that all creation was subservient to him and created for him), fostered belief in man's role as a steward. Finally we must note the slow accumulation of observations, without any necessary religious or philosophical applications, of changes, beneficial or harmful by human standards, which man brings about through the ordinary routines of life in an essentially rural and pre-industrial age: cutting down trees, draining swamps, making polders to keep out the sea, grazing sheep or cattle in mountain meadows, killing fruit- or seed-eating birds or intrusive carnivores. These general ideas are part of the cultural heritage of Western civilization. Many of them probably owed their origin to religious or philosophical generalizations made from ordinary daily occupations.

IV

The eighteenth century was notable for its interests in both man and nature; in the nineteenth, the intensification of interest in nature and in all life was remarkable. There are so many skeins that I doubt any historian of ideas could satisfactorily unravel them, but for our purposes even a selective outline has its merits. Among the religious, artistic, philosophic, and literary trends of the century, there is that intense interest in and preoccupation with the natural world that is so characteristic of the Romantic Movement, although it might be better to omit that deeply intrenched term and refer simply to the remarkable body of thought and artistic activity concerned with the world of nature and man's relation to it. Several attitudes toward the natural world were in a direct line of descent from the classical and the Biblical world; the idea of the holiness of nature, its harmonies and beauties actually and symbolically offering incontrovertible evidences of the existence of God, was still very much alive in the eighteenth century, reaching an apogee in Bernardin de St. Pierre's *Études de la Nature* (1784). It was expressed even more religiously with remarkable but unexciting vigor in the *Génie du Christianisme* of Chateaubriand and was ever-present in the reverent nature writings of the early Ruskin, especially in *Modern Painters* and the autobiographical *Praeterita.* This natural theology, this physico-theology, carried the design argument far into the century, and, as Lyell saw, it was a most formidable opponent of the new concept of interrelationships in nature offered by Darwin.[4] Others have seen the essence of the Romantic view toward nature in its exaltation of the sublime, the wild, the far removed, and the untouched. This is true, but the delimitation is too restrictive. A nature which was close to man, the humanized landscapes of Europe and the Near East, landscapes with historical associations were also loved. In his *Journey from Paris to Jerusalem, 1806–07,* Chateaubriand confesses that his early fascinations with loneliness and the wilderness of the New World was succeeded by a love of Italy, Greece, and the Holy Land with their ruins, and other strong associations with the past. Landscapes thus literally enshrined and embodied the past. In addition to the wild, the sublime, or the landscapes redolent of history, there was also the rural landscape in which the natural life of the peasant contrasted sharply with the metallic and mechanical artificialities of the city. Furthermore, there was a Romantic view of the city and its surroundings, in which old and historic quarters and landmarks were prized above the aesthetics of progress and demolition. One need only read the chapter in Victor Hugo's *Notre Dame* on the bird's-eye view of Paris, or recall Hugo's efforts to save the old Gothic cathedrals, monuments, and parts of historic Paris. Even technology becomes a member of the brotherhood. In *Art and the Industrial Revolution* (1947), Francis D. Klingender discusses that *enfant terrible,* the machine; his charming and illuminating illustrations of machines, railroads, forges, and mines in the landscape assume an eerie, mysterious quality. In George Inness' painting, *The Lackawanna Valley* (1855), the gentle locomotive, with its soft, white, curling smoke, runs on the graceful curving track, laid down in a quiet pastoral valley with a roundhouse in the distance. Of it, Leo Marx says, "It is a striking representation of the idea that machine technology is a proper part of the landscape."[5] The shepherdlike figure on the hillside looks like early nineteenth-century paintings of shepherds on hillsides enjoying a view of Basel. The locomotive is so much a part of its natural surroundings that it seems God had created it, too, in the beginning.

The writers, artists, poets of the Romantic Movement explored, not in a scientific (at least in its rigorous sense, though many were aware of science) but in an aesthetic and emotional way, the nature of the external world. They often idealized the wild and the sublime, but there was also love of landscapes in which heroes had lived and of rivers whose waters they had drunk, of peasant huts and picturesque villages, of beauties like the Drachenfels at Winterthur on the Rhine, whose stony cliffs were saved in 1836 from the quarrymen because of their beauty, their dramatic qualities and mythological associations. There are charming Romantic pictures of this part of the Rhine in the municipal museum at Bonn. These ideas and the men who propounded them were important early stimuli for the preservation of monuments and landscapes: the old part of the city, certain quarters, squares, and town halls, even for the still toylike machines in the countryside.

The Romantic Movement had a strong organic as opposed to a mechanical bias, as illustrated in the nature themes in the music of Beethoven, Brahms, and Smetana. The Movement also had a historical rather than positivist and progressive orientation, as revealed in the enthusiasm for the preservation and conservation of the treasures of the past, whether artifacts or works of nature. One could write a book on the efforts made in Germany and in Switzerland alone to save remarkable specimens of boulders transported by glaciers and left in place by their retreat. The movement for the protection and preservation of buildings, quarters, entire towns, of natural objects like old trees with sentimental associations, threatened plant and animal species, owes much to the Romantic period. Wordsworth meditated on Tintern Abbey; he also was interested in the preservation of the Lake District. In France, the painters of the Barbizon school were active in saving the Forest of Fontainebleau, protected by a law of Napoleon III in 1861. This conserving and preserving tendency of the Romantic artists and writers and others of like mind has been very important in the modern history of attitudes toward nature in Western civilization.

There is one more important point about the Romantic Movement: This was the reawakening interest in perception of environment. In Alexander von Humboldt's great work, the *Kosmos,* he remarks that there is a distinction (I do not believe it a correct one) between the contributions of Buffon and those of Rousseau, Bernardin de Saint Pierre, and Chateaubriand. Buffon, he said, lacked that awareness of the power of nature to awaken feelings and emotions which was so conspicuous in the writings of others.[6] It would be absurd to say that the thinkers of the Romantic Movement invented communion with nature, *Naturgefühl,* the evocative power of nature, since there are many examples among the pre-romantics and in the classical world, but it is true that in this period, there was a great interest in perception of the environment and in its subtler influences on the mind, the feelings, moods, emotions. Color, light, sound were the vital ingredients of this fresh look at the external world. The themes of environmental perception, the distinction between what an environment is and what people think it is, what it can be transformed into by imagination and fancy are the beginnings of a modern interest in nature transcending practical concerns and everyday routines. We are today in the midst of a similar concern. Ideas concerning nature assume a new importance in this movement, as if they were independent dignitaries, no longer mercenaries to be strewn throughout the pages of poetry, travel, philosophy, art history, and theology.

V

For another part of our story, we may now turn to an entirely different body of thought. One important discovery of modern times is that the earth has a history, or, more correctly, that it has a more factual history than that of the antediluvian, the flood, the postdiluvian periods given in the Bible. That the earth has a history different from that given in Genesis has a bearing on our theme, because it alters the role of man and his place in history. In the *Epoques de la nature* (1778), for example, Count Buffon divided earth history into seven epochs, the first six of which had passed without any human witnesses. In the seventh and last epoch, man appears and with the passage of time creates his own history embodied in a civilization.[7] Not merely a passive observer, man himself is an active agent who assists nature. Buffon's conception is different from that in Genesis, where man is also a latecomer crowning the acts of creation. In Genesis the dominion over the rest of nature is bestowed upon man as a creative act of God, whereas in Buffon, man's transforming power, similarly bestowed, begins late in the earth's history and becomes really effective only with civilization, not with primitive life.

Let us linger a moment on this matter of the earth's history. In James Hutton's *Theory of the Earth* (1795), universally acknowledged to be a revolutionary work in historical geology, one is struck with the emphasis on processes which have brought the earth to its present condition. Among them, Hutton stresses the extensive erosion which water, given enough time, can bring about. The flow of water on the surface introduces two further considerations: the relation of mountains or uplands to valleys or lowlands, and the nature of stream courses—whether they are straight or sinuous, or whether in their upper courses their banks are naturally lined with vegetation to regularize stream flow. It is noteworthy that Hutton makes extensive use of the field work of those who have studied the Alps in considering these questions. The tendency of the water, given sufficient time, is gradually to eliminate great altitudinal contrasts until the earth's surface becomes level. The tendency thus would be for mountains to gradually disappear, and for lowlands, especially deltas, to be built up. Here we have the description of purely natural processes, observable in the present, fashioning the earth's relief. In essence, it is the uniformitarian theory, the processes of the past are like those of the present, and the flow of water is one of the most powerful. For the most part, the only role man plays in Hutton's scheme is that of an observer. To Hutton, a believer in the design argument, these processes are the results of a planning deity who has the welfare of mankind in mind. For of what use are fertile soils in inaccessible mountains when streams can transport them to the plains where they can be properly used?[8] The Huttonian scheme, like the concept of a balance and equilibrium in nature, which will be discussed later, required a long time for the small, gradual changes with their enormous cumulative effects to take place, but the important point here is that one can also look upon the scheme as a model, a standard, a measuring device for the study of change.

In one significant sense, Hutton's views were less advanced than those of Count Buffon in 1778. Hutton did not consider the questions of human agency in these processes, avoiding, too, the problem of the uniqueness of man. Buffon had considered both. In the *Epoques de la nature,* he says we cannot know what the earth was like in ancient times by observing it in settled countries, for now it is as much the work of man as it is of nature; we must go to newly discovered virgin lands to get an idea of what the epoch before man was like, remembering also that before it there were earlier epochs still. The humanized world we see about us is a creation of civilized not of primitive man. In a remarkable passage, Buffon says that half-savage man living in the so-called golden age never doubted the time would come when he would "imprint his ideas on the entire face of the universe." The changes he makes in nature are different because he differs prodigiously from the animals, not in body but in a God-imparted mind and spirit. Buffon here anticipates a concept developed in the twentieth century, chiefly by his fellow Frenchman, the Jesuit priest, Teilhard de Chardin, that the thin, organic layer of the surface of the earth has become a noosphere, the sphere of reflective thought, "the thinking layer," which man has now spread over the biosphere.[9] To Buffon, the seventh epoch, that of man, was a period in which new processes were coming into being, not those induced by volcanos, floods, and streams but by self-conscious minds; man's adaptability, and virtual ubiquity ("since the perfection of navigation, wherever man has penetrated, he everywhere has found men") makes changing the earth on an ever-widening scale possible; and man-ordered environments replace those of nature. This is one way of looking at history: in the nineteenth and twentieth centuries it has become the subject matter of historical geography.

VI

Like Buffon's *Epoques de la nature,* Sir Charles Lyell's *Principles of Geology* (1830–33) examines the role of human agency in modifying the earth; it, too, is a precious text from an essentially pre-industrial period in which modern theories of the nature of life, its origin and development were beginning to take shape. Lyell agreed with Hutton that the earth had a long history. He played down the importance of man as a modifier of the earth because he believed man had appeared very late in earth history. Man, however, is a participant in natural processes, not merely an observer, as Hutton saw him, but he thought man to be such a latecomer that his ascendancy was scarcely "felt by the brutes." The coming of man posed, however, an important question: Is his introduction into the life of the planet of so revolutionary a character as to destroy our confidence in the uniformity of nature?[10] An affirmative answer would undermine the arguments advanced by Hutton and other adherents of or sympathizers with the uniformitarian theory—that is, that the processes operating in the past to form the relief of the earth are essentially the same as those which are observable here and now. Man's activities would be unique in their effects; hence current processes in which he participates could not be extrapolated in order to know the earth's state in past ages. Lyell's answer to the question is in the negative, and it is arrived at, essentially, by denying, as far as modifications of the natural world are concerned, the existence of that great gulf between human and brute action so conspicuous in the social world.[11] One might say that beavers and men alike build dams; men go to libraries, beavers do not—or not voluntarily. The effects on the natural world are comparable, their activities in the social world are not.

Lyell thus minimizes the uniqueness of man as a modifier of nature. It is possible to exaggerate the importance of man. Just because man, alone of all the modifying agents, is rational, is no reason to believe, Lyell argues, that his effect on nature will differ in great degree from that of other animals. "We are apt hastily to infer, that the effects of a rational and an irrational species considered merely as *physical agents,* will differ almost as much as the faculties by which their actions are directed."[12]

Yet Lyell considers at some length the effects of man on animate and inanimate nature and one wonders how—using only his own evidence—he was so conservative in his earlier views. (Later in life he changed them radically.) Possibly he saw a threat to concepts of the regularity and constancy of nature if man were seen as an early, often capricious, unthinking, but effective agent in environmental change. If he were, it would reveal the folly of separating the study of human from physical geography. It would also reveal the enormous complexities involved in the study of plant and animal geography, to say nothing of inanimate nature, not only in the present but in the past as well. Lyell tried valiantly to interpret human action well within the normal spectrum of changes induced by other agencies. Man has been an important agent in the diffusion of plants and animals, and his unintentional disseminations could exceed those done purposefully; large areas of cultivated land could act as stabilizers preventing migrations and interchanges of flora and fauna that would otherwise occur. Like Buffon, Lyell saw the selective role of man in controlling other forms of life; for example, increasing the numbers of useful quadrupeds and exterminating the harmful; the unconscious and involuntary role of man in the multiplication of "inimical species" through introductions such as that of the rat into the New World, but this role is "strictly analogous to that of the inferior animals."[13] He anticipated ideas which appeared later in the century that man tends to encourage monoculture and in our own that he is a simplifier of ecosystems. The latter suggestion, yet unproved, made, I believe, originally by Charles S. Elton in *The Ecology of Invasions by Animals and Plants* (1958), could become a decisive concept in the crucial question of maintaining the habitability of the earth for human purposes in the future. "Man is, in truth," Lyell says, "continually striving to diminish the natural diversity of the *stations* of animals and plants in every country, and to reduce them all to a small number fitted for species of economical use."[14] If human populations grow and distribute themselves, the resulting settlements displace other habitants; a human community takes over a biotic community; here Lyell calls attention to an important mechanism of extirpation. In justice to Lyell, his failure at first to put stronger emphasis on man's agency may be due to his belief that man has come recently into the world, that "the effects of his agency are only beginning to be felt," and, finally, that cultural geography was not his subject. Lyell has an optimistic interpretation of man's agency in his attempt to keep this child of nature within the family circle. There is no reason to "repine," he said, about the havoc we create by our exterminations. "We have only to reflect that in thus obtaining possession of the earth by conquest, and defending our acquisitions by force, we exercise no exclusive prerogative." Man is only doing what other forms of life do.[15]

Man possesses selective power, too, in influencing geological processes. Lyell believed man cannot significantly control the degradation of land, but he can control the distribution of sediment, especially at deltas; he has little control over igneous or aqueous agents, but he can alter habitats by drainage. So he is not only an observer, student, and disseminator but also a leveling agent, but insignificant compared with the great physical forces, water and fire.[16] Yet, with all his awareness, his recognition that man is a single widely distributed species of superior power, a self-distributor, Lyell in 1830 does not want to grant a revolutionary character to human agency. He obviously wants to see man as a continuator not as a revolutionary, a successor to other agents, perhaps long since extinct, in the history of the earth.

VII

It is now time to consider some of the implications of the Darwinian theory of evolution and its bearing on the question of human agency. In the conception of nature which succeeded the Biblical, there was infinitely more earth history without man than with him. This shift in point of view introduced new problems and forced revisions in old ones. Could one now maintain that the whole of previous history was a prologue for the coming of man, as the successive acts of God in the six days of creation had been? Was nature created for man? What was nature like independent of man?

In Darwinian evolutionary theory, interrelationships in the world of inanimate and animate nature also existed long before the coming of man. It was thought that, barring worldwide catastrophies, this world of nature tends toward a balance or equilibrium. Historically, this is one of the most important concepts, with modern revisions and corrections, upon which our attitude toward the natural environment is based. I refer here to the idea of a balance or equilibrium in nature as it developed in evolutionary theory—not to the time when it was thought to be the product of design. The web of complex relations, Darwin said, was such that "in the long run the forces are so nicely balanced that the face of nature remains uniform for long periods."[17] Such a concept suggests questions like the character of nature before the coming of man, and the problem of determining what occurs in a situation free of man's influences or intrusions. It calls attention to the dangers of ignoring the activity of man in the study of biotic communities; a point made by Marston Bates, in the *Forest and the Sea,* and the need of establishing protected areas in order to study ecological situations as free from human influence as possible. It also calls for the study of the exact nature of human transformations and how they might differ from others. Thus during the second half of the nineteenth century, a concept of nature was being fashioned under the stimulus of the Darwinian theory, and simultaneously there was a growing interest in and concern about human intrusions into the natural world. These trends, as we shall see, converge dramatically in the work of George P. Marsh.

It may be well to expand a bit on this conception of nature which developed in the nineteenth century as a result of Darwin's work. It had various names, perhaps the best known being a biocenose, a term the German zoologist, Möbius, applied to the biotic community of an oyster bed. In general, it broadened and deepened the idea of interrelationships in nature. This was an extremely important development because it provided a concept of nature which would serve as a rough guide for interpreting the extent and character of human modifications of the natural world. It complemented Hutton's model. Nature was likened to a web, a pattern, a balance, an equilibrium in which the idea is developed that some slight disturbance in one part of the web or balance might reveal itself in far-off parts of the system. In 1910, J. Arthur Thomson wrote of nature that it "has a woven pattern which science seeks to read, each science following the threads of a particular colour.... There is a changing pattern in the web, becoming more complex as the ages pass; and *this is evolution.* But the essential idea of a web is that of interlinking and ramifying." "The more we know of our surroundings the more we realize that nature is a vast system of linkages, that isolation is impossible."[18] It is noteworthy that Thomson sees evolution in terms of a developing pattern of interrelationships; in thus viewing it, he was unusual, for the ecological aspects of the Darwinian theory have not been discussed with nearly the thoroughness as have the phylogenetic. In such a philosophy of interrelationships and interconnectedness in nature, human modifications of the environment are not discrete, single, unrelated events, but intrusions in a network of interrelationships. It is true that such interpretations did not have to await the Darwinian concept; in the writings of John Evelyn in the seventeenth century and in those of many natural historians of the eighteenth, human interferences in the biological world are seen as interferences in the stable and harmonious interrelationships of the animate and inanimate world.

From the late seventeenth century to the publication of *On the Origin of Species*, there has been a sustained interest in these interrelationships—in what we now call ecology.[19] In the nature theologies of John Ray, the botanist and natural historian, and of the Rev. William Derham, early ecology was brought to a high level, using the argument from design. The world was a fit place to live in—not a misshapen creation of God adapted to the sinfulness of man. The triad of mountains, streams, and valleys was part of this fitness; so were land and sea relationships because they were vital to the hydrologic cycle, and so was the inclination of the earth on its axis, for this increased the habitable parts of the globe and caused the seasons. None of these was separate; each was related to the other; they formed a network of interrelationships in which individual life forms were born and died. Species were created from the beginning in such a way that they wre adapted to one another; adaptation was a key idea because in a designed creation everything was adapted to its milieu. It was a kind of religious functionalism. Constructs of nature based on interrelationships, adaptations, harmony, and equilibrium continued, with the idea of design, in the philosophies of nature of Buffon and of von Humboldt, but for modern thought the decisive step was taken by Darwin.

Study and observation of human activities actually helped in formulating the concept. To Darwin, the great force of human power in interfering in the plant and animal world (artificial selection) highlighted the infinitely greater power of nature in natural selection. Clearings made by cutting down or firing forests made dramatic changes; but afterward, if left alone, the forest grew back and nature restored the balance. Then there were the examples of the fences and the Scotch fir, and the famous cats-to-clover chain. In the first, Darwin contrasts two kinds of heaths, the unenclosed and the enclosed. On the former, there are a few clumps of Scotch fir, but they are in great numbers on the latter, the difference between the two being that the enclosed field kept out cattle that perpetually browsed down seedlings and little trees. In the cats-to-clover chain, bumble bees visit the red clover. The number of bees is regulated by the field mice who destroy their combs and nests, and the field mice are regulated by the cats, which are more numerous near small towns and villages.[20] These trends, from Ray's *Wisdom of God Manifested in the Works of Creation* (1691) to Darwin and then from him to the present concept of an ecosystem, made possible new insights into the relation of human cultures to the environment as a whole, into the nature of the history of human settlement, into man's directive force over other forms of life. These opportunities are grasped by George P. Marsh.

VIII

Thirty-four years separated the publication of Lyell's *Principles of Geology* and Marsh's *Man and Nature* in 1864. We can compare them, granting that they were writing on different subjects, Marsh devoting a book to what Lyell had devoted a few pages. Then, too, their backgrounds were different—Lyell being a geologist, Marsh a lawyer, politician, student of literature and languages and American minister to Italy when *Man and Nature* was published. Lyell had tried his best to keep mankind behaving within the general framework of the other processes changing nature. Yet within 34 years there appeared a work in dramatic contrast with Lyell's, showing in unexampled detail, the unique, often irreversible, power of man in modifying the fact of nature, a more forceful and grim statement of the case than Buffon's. Lyell himself changed his mind later in life; in his travels to the United States, he had observed near Milledgeville, Georgia, the effects of accelerated gully erosion and in a letter to Marsh, dated September 22, 1865, he wrote that he "had erred in supposing man's geographical impact was no greater than that of brute animals."[21]

I do not wish to detract from the pleasure that readers of this article will find in *Man and Nature* and in David Lowenthal's biography of Marsh, in which it becomes abundantly clear why Marsh wrote such a book. I will confine myself, therefore, to a few general observations pertinent to our theme. Marsh wrote at a time when there was a deep concern (already apparent in the eighteenth century) over the relation of deforestation to soil erosion and climatic change. In Europe, especially in the Mediterranean and Alpine lands, there was widespread alarm concerning the denuding of mountain areas by shepherds to make meadows. (In 1876 the celebrated French architect and controversial restorer of Carcassonne, Viollet-le-duc, wrote an eloquent chapter on this subject in his study *Le Massif de Mont Blanc.*) The French engineer Fabre had published a work on torrent control in 1797; in his pages, man, in the role of a shepherd, is a far more destructive being than in Buffon's *Epochs of Nature* published almost twenty years before, and an infinitely more powerful agent than Lyell described in 1830.[22] What these men were saying—Fabre, Marsh, and later many of the highly imaginative students of Alpine forests like Alexander Surrell—was that a great physical relationship on earth, that of mountain to plain, upland to lowland, including the streams that joined them, was poorly understood. So was the role of the mountain shepherd as an accelerator of torrents which carried down the slopes soil, stones, and large boulders. Viollet-le-duc later spoke for many: There is no protection for the high mountains, and goats and shepherds are often the villains. Here was a thorough and unsparing analysis of the shepherd with no idealization of his pipes, fires, folk songs. Men in the nineteenth century did not discover deforestation, torrents, and soil erosion, but many saw the great importance of the highland-lowland relationships, a physical relationship enmeshed in systems of law, custom and tenure.

This was the kind of literature available to Marsh, who was an imaginative synthesizer of technical reports, often of local application, Marsh places himself in opposition to two important bodies of thought: Lyell's thesis on the weakness of man, and geographic determinism. *Man and Nature* was written in order to state the case for the overwhelming power of man, once the whole span of human history is considered and the cumulative force over time of changes in the environment is understood. Geographic determinism, with a long tradition dating back to classical times, had eloquent defenders in Marsh's time. In general, the determinists of varying hue thought that geographical elements—climate, soil, relief—were molders, or, if not these, strong determinants of the way of life of peoples and nations. Marsh turned the tables: He did not study nature's effect on man, but man's effect on nature. Such a reversal of roles was neither bombast nor rhetoric; it involved a fundamentally different conception of man's place in nature. Geographical determinism tended to stress what is passive in man and culture: mountains make men brave, island people become sailors, uniform deserts of limitless sameness engender monotheism. Marsh's use of the idea of man as a geographic force meant that entirely different matters were stressed: man's long-term and cumulative influences on the land, such as cutting down forests, diverting streams, domesticating plants and animals.

Man and Nature is written as a history. The sequence in man's occupation of the earth is the domestication of plants and animals, the attack on the forests, control over the unstable waters, and control of the sands. This is not the place for a detailed discussion of each of these developments, but a few observations are in order. Marsh, like Darwin, wrote at a time when there was intense interest in plant and animal domestication. Domestication is one of the clearest, most spectacular, evidences of man's ability to control the kind, nature, and quality of other forms of life. Buffon had appreciated its significance. Moreover, the successes of eighteenth-century plant and animal breeders were fresh in mind. Domestication could be a technique, but, to Marsh, it was much more; it was a significant extension of human power. Domestic animals (like the dog, the goat, the sheep) also become agents of change within human enclaves. Domesticated plants and animals vastly increased the areas of the earth's surface under direct human manipulation. One is reminded of Buffon's characterization of the shepherd dog as man's great helpmeet on the road to civilization. Without him, and the other animals who deserted the animal world for the human, the whole venture in dominion would have failed. Furthermore, the study of man's selective influence on plant and animal life leads into the question of man as a direct or indirect, conscious or unconscious, exterminator of plants and animals. Earlier, Buffon and Lyell, like Marsh, had seen that extermination need not involve direct killing, but was often caused by the elimination or drastic modification of habitats, particularly in the long-settled lands. As the century wore on, the literature on extermination of plants, animals, and human life, especially of primitive peoples in the United States, Africa, and the Pacific increased.

There is nothing, except the cold, metallic, computerized obliterations of life characteristic of our times, to match the remorseless extermination of life in the nineteenth century. This ruthless obliteration produced some of our most poignant accounts of primitive peoples, and stimulated ethnology to record the life of primitive peoples before they "disappeared." There was much bland talk about civilized people displacing the "savage." On one hand, there was greed; on the other, a philosophical conviction, enforced by the insufferable smugness of the believers in the idea of progress, that there was a great gulf between civilized man and the savage. Both greed and philosophy doomed primitive peoples and the environments they created, for it was another myth that savages were slaves, but civilized men controllers of their environment. The merciless killing of birds for their plumes, the ghastly slaughter of the bison, the cult of the rifle and the big-game hunt are familiar nineteenth-century themes. With the extermination of so many human beings, plants, and animals, from the muskets of the French Revolution to the napalm of the Vietnam war, the great wonder is that there is not more concern than there is about mankind's attitudes toward all life. No wonder Albert Schweitzer wrote so much about awe of life (*Ehrfurcht vor dem Leben*).

Marsh wrote extensively, often with that trenchant indignation that is so admirable in him, of the transfer, modification and extirpation of plants and animals. Broadly speaking, the processes described by Marsh and others at this time were, for the most part, old and traditional. They described a world changed essentially by the practices of peasants, farmers, shepherds, and pre-industrial city dwellers. There is no sentimentalizing about rural virtues, peasant care of the land, shepherds and their flocks. Marsh writes (largely, but not completely) of a pre-industrial world changed remorselessly by simple tools and simple men. He also used the concept of a balance or equilibrium in nature as a kind of model, a measure for seeing human action in perspective. The concept assumed a new role, which with revisions and modifications, it retains to this day. Before Marsh, the idea of a unity, balance, and equilibrium in nature was less involved with human modifications of the environment. In the design argument, the concept is mainly a religious one; it has to do with the evidences of God's existence and purpose. With less teleological thinkers like Buffon and von Humboldt, it is a unifying principle by which one tries to understand the unity and diversity in nature. So it is with Darwin, but with Marsh's strong insistence on the dichotomy of man and nature, man is seen as an intruder and disturber of the balance. In this way, the concept of balance or imbalance becomes a means of understanding the character of the intrusions. This concept of a balance in nature, a nature which is self-healing, self-restorative even in the face of great natural catastrophies, but fragile and often helpless when confronted by man, was the basis of Marsh's pessimism; his work, without question, is the longest, most closely argued and sustained work that has yet appeared from a single hand which postulates the possibility of the earth becoming uninhabitable for man because of his activities. If we bear in mind man's uniqueness, ubiquity, his intelligence as well as his ignorance his tendency either to occupy land for a long time, as in the Near East or in China, for millennia, or to move on from one destroyed place to the next, then one realizes the possibilities for acceleration and irreversibility of man-induced changes. Irreversibility—this is the grim significance of the contrast between human and brute action. The argument also rests on the long-term view, on present use and concern for posterity.

Finally, Marsh recognized the great educational value of comparison. Perhaps no European, no person who had lived all his life in a country or region which had been settled for centuries or millennia, could have written *Man and Nature* as well as he. The America of his day was no pristine, primordial land, but it still seemed so compared to Europe, and he could make vivid contrasts between the Old World and the New. He could use these contrasts as lessons, largely unheeded, to his countrymen, and he could make a case for stewardship and preservation for posterity.

Thus, in the nineteenth century, and especially in Marsh's *Man and Nature,* the slow almost imperceptible action of most forces (except catastrophic agencies like earthquakes and volcanoes) are in striking contrast with the acceleration of processes for which man is responsible. Similar observations had been made before by scientific travelers of the late eighteenth and early nineteenth centuries. What could be more dramatic —if one were in this historical frame of mind—than seeing with one's own eyes what a European axe in the hands of a woodsman could do in a few days—even a few hours—in a forest which to all appearances had existed in an almost unchanging equilibrium since the creation? That man can be an accelerator of processes changing the surface of the earth was overwhelmingly shown throughout the century as a result of the invasion of sparsely settled lands by Europeans with their values and technologies. Buffon's observation that newly discovered lands resemble the former appearances of the earth more than do present inhabited lands like Europe, took on new meaning. In America, especially since the end of the Civil War, the primitive and inhabited states might not be far apart, as illustrated in the Currier and Ives print, *Across the Continent.*

Environmental transformation in the nineteenth century —one of continuous cumulative changes in the Old World, accelerating violent ones in the New—was a harbinger of what, with vastly increased populations, was to come in the twentieth century. Marsh wrote part of the story, but wrote too early to tell all of it. It is a great pity that in human affairs so many accurate judgments are made, and there is so little dissemination and awareness of them. There has been a large and perceptive literature on nature and man's effect on it from the Euro-American world, Africa, the Near East, Central Asia, India, China, which remains unsynthesized to this day and which had accumulated before the beginning of World War I. Many writings about "the environmental crisis" today give the impression that an unprecedented awareness is coming into being, that environmental changes are of recent origin rather than of recent acceleration, that the past was simple and the present complex, and that man is now for the first time affecting the whole earth.

IX

Up to this point, I have been concerned in the main with natural processes and the non-urban world; in order to throw further light on the development of attitudes toward nature, I wish to say a few words about a very large and very complex subject—the creation of industrial landscapes. By this term, I mean something quite concrete and literal: the appearance of areas in which industry dominates, in which the chimney, the mine, the smokestack, and the locomotive become so prominent that it is they and not the natural scenery—with the cottage, the rural inn, the mill on the stream—that give a landscape its distinctive characteristics. It is the beginning of a new way of organizing space, sharpening more than ever the already existing contrasts between the city and the country, provoking both fear and admiration of the machine and its cultural effects, strengthening an already existing literature on alienation in city life which many saw as a consequence of mankind's separation from nature. I have already mentioned

Klingender's *Industrial Art in England,* whose descriptions from contemporary sources and whose admirable illustrations show this new industrial landscape coming into being. My favorite description, however, is the opening paragraph of T.S. Ashton's *The Industrial Revolution.* In a few sentences, Ashton gives one the feeling of one kind of environment being replaced by another. The scene is in England, where industrial landscapes of the modern type first appeared.

"In the short span of years between the accession of George III [1760] and that of his son, William IV [1830], the face of England changed. Areas that for centuries had been cultivated as open fields, or had lain untended as common pasture, were hedged or fenced; hamlets grew into populous towns; and chimney stacks rose to dwarf the ancient spires. Highroads were made—straighter, stronger, and wider than those evil communications that had corrupted the good manners of travelers in the days of Defoe. The North and Irish Seas, and the navigable reaches of the Mersey, Ouse, Trent, Severn, Thames, Forth, and Clyde were joined together by threads of still water. In the north the first iron rails were laid down for the new locomotives, and steam packets began to ply on the estuaries and the narrow seas."

Thus we see a unique landscape being created. It was to grow and assume gigantic form; its size, extent, and uniqueness engendered new attitudes toward the rural countryside in which human influences were relatively diffuse, as contrasted with the city where they were concentrated and overpowering. It is most important to observe that there is a further sharpening of the ancient contrasts between city and country because the visual aspect of the industrial city is vastly different. This new contrast begins another chapter in the man-nature relationship. It is true that one can find descriptions of air and water pollution in early literature (John Evelyn's vigorous description of it in seventeenth-century London in

Fumifugium[23] is a famous example), but in the nineteenth century, there were new and pungent smells. Indignant letters to the editor protest the railroad which will cut through an old village, or complain that streams now have weird colors. It is the beginning of a literature in part coming from the Romantics, in part from scientists, reformers, and individual observers like Dickens and Ruskin. Some of it is devoted to industrial landscapes, a literature in which we are enmeshed today with the difference that the critique of megalopolis no longer seems to be derived from Frankenstein fears, but from the prospect of a mindless technological society.

Thirty-four years separated the publication dates of Marsh's *Man and Nature* and Lyell's *Principles of Geology*, and twenty-five separate the accession of William IV (mentioned in the quotation from Ashton) from the description of Coketown in Dickens' *Hard Times* (1854). What was Coketown? It was "a town of red brick, or of brick that would have been red if the smoke and ashes had allowed it; but as matters stood it was a form of unnatural red and black like the painted face of a savage." Observe here the words which express something both artificial and uncivilized. "It was a town of machinery and tall chimneys," whose smoke is likened to serpents which trail "themselves forever and ever, and never get uncoiled." Against the disfigured red brick are set the black canal and the purple-dyed river, vast piles of buildings with rattling and trembling windows "where the piston of the steam-engine worked monotonously up and down like the head of an elephant in a state of melancholy madness," adding the qualities of monotony, melancholy, and insanity to conditions already known as artificial and uncivilized. Uniformity and drab similarity appear in large and small streets alike, traversed by people equally uniform and drab, and people "to whom every day was the same as yesterday and tomorrow and every year the counterpart of the last and next." Add now cyclic mindlessness. Coketown is a place of industry and busyness; "severely workful." A chapel is "a pious warehouse of red brick." So uniform is everything that the "jail might have been the infirmary, the infirmary might have been the jail; the town hall might have been either or both, or anything else. . . . Fact, fact, fact, everywhere in the material aspect of the town; fact, fact, fact, everywhere in the immaterial" and in this world of facts, "what you couldn't state in figures, or show to be purchaseable in the cheapest market and salable in the dearest, was not, and never would be, world without end, Amen." Is it any wonder that *Das Kapital* was written in a period of growing industrial landscapes dominated by a laissez-faire philosophy sympathetic to Mandeville's famous pronouncement in *The Fable of the Bees* that private vices are public virtues, or that one of the most sensitive studies of the industrial city, *The Condition of the Working Class in England in 1844,* came from the pen of Friedrich Engels? Similar descriptions were soon to be written for other fledgling Manchesters on the continent and in the United States.

In the *City and History,* Lewis Mumford has observed that Coketown and similar industrial creations had the important role of evoking their own literature of protest,[24] for fundamental change had occurred in an ancient relationship. How far back this contrast between the "artificial" city and the "natural" countryside goes I do not know; in the classical world, it appears in the writings of Horace, Varro, and Columella; the eighteenth century is full of it, and Rousseau did not invent the contrast with manifestos from Vevey on Lake Geneva about the artificial life of Paris. But now the contrasts become starker; engravings of artificial cities of the eighteenth century seem to a modern eye simple, colorful, leisurely, but no doubt they are idealized.

X

John Ruskin, in his long and productive career, was aware of many of the developments I have been speaking of in this paper. Hopefully, Kenneth Clark's recent book of selections from his writings, *Ruskin Today,* will revive interest in him. He was intimately acquainted with many highly contrasting landscapes—of Britain, Switzerland, France, and Italy. As a young man, Ruskin associated himself closely with natural theology,[25] and his ideas on God's design in nature are distinguishable from hundreds of other expressions in his and in earlier centuries. They are squarely in the center of a tradition, already strong in the Stoics as well as in the Psalms, that sees the universe as the handiwork of God. Wordsworth was an early mentor and Tintern Abbey seems like a new green Bible for Ruskin. His interpretation of nature is intensely anthropocentric, and he is constantly concerned with the usefulness of nature to man. He idealizes the nature unimproved by man and ridicules the ordered landscape gardens.[26] A lifelong critic of railroads and railroad-station designs, his pages abound in indignant remarks about the "iron roads" which are "tearing up the surface of Europe."[27] He bemoans the disappearance of the old in cities and in towns (he is an enemy of restorers like Viollet-le-duc) not because he is an antiquarian, but because the old is a landmark of the past, a living part of civilization.[28] But he is no admirer of the bogus picturesque which conceals poverty and misery.[29]

Later in life, clouds appear on the horizon; he is far less infatuated with nature, whether it is Wordsworth's or anyone else's; he becomes increasingly outraged with the exploitation of labor and the evils of the industrial world and the landscapes it created. He seems to have regarded his early deep immersion in nature as a retreat from the world of man. For him the railroad is an example and a symbol; its coming marks the end of travel because on a train one becomes like a parcel being sent from one station to another.[30] An age like our own, plagued by smog, freeways, trucks, lobbies of concrete makers and auto manufacturers, can afford to be wistful about railroads and take leave of Ruskin's sentiments here! In youth, too, he rejected the idea that scenery must have human associations; he was enthralled by the beauty of the organic world. But there is no idealization of rural life; he writes of the misery and poverty of the Swiss mountain peasantry. He knows about torrents and shepherds, for he is a great lover of mountains—of "mountain gloom" and "mountain glory."[31] In an increasing preoccupation with the human world, he becomes disenchanted with the wild, the unimproved in nature and prefers landscapes redolent of human associations. Nature is disappearing from the towns, and it is the function of architecture to take its place.[32]

One's admiration increases in reading Ruskin's letters, written in later life and in old age, protesting social injustice, water pollution, the destruction of natural scenery, the obliteration of the old by the shoddy new, the indifference of the ruling classes.[33] In a letter to his father in 1863, he wrote, "There are not two men in the Parliament of England who would not be more angry if the Emperor of Russia stopped their partridge-shooting than if he murdered every soul in his dominions."[34] Ruskin's writings are pertinent to a history of ideas concerning man and nature during the last one-hundred years in Western civilization. Parochial as he could be, he had a broad vision on these matters, broader I think than Wordsworth, Emerson, Thoreau, Carlyle, Whitman, or Arnold.

XI

On the threshold of the nineteenth century, Wordsworth wrote as if the English pastoral landscape might go on forever. To him the poet is still the best interpreter of man's relation to nature. It is in "the humble and rustic life" that the essential passions of the heart are incorporated with the beautiful, permanent forms of life, and he sees no conflict between the poet and the scientist. They seem able to go hand in hand down the corridors of time.

At the end of the century, Rudyard Kipling was writing stories which required words like trolley, lattice-girder, truss, railroad line, traveling crane, rivet. In the "Bridge-Builders," the engineer Finlayson surveys the changes his bridge over the Ganges have made in an ancient land, and in another story, ".007," personified locomotives reveal in intimate conversation their rivalries, prides, and false prides, their feelings of inadequacy, and condescensions in a world of Pullman cars, freight yards, and roundhouses.[35]

In the 1830's, Lyell had played down the power of man; by 1909, two American geologists, T.C. Chamberlain and R.D. Salisbury were saying: "Lyell long since urged that the direct work of man in changing the face of the earth was slight compared with that of the contemporaneous inorganic agencies.... There is justness in this view, but it needs qualification. It is to be observed that the mental era has but just begun, and that its effects are increasing with a rapidity quite phenomenal when measured by the slow place of most geologic events. The excavations and transportation of material today show an enormous advance on those of Lyell's day, which was, geologically speaking, but a moment ago." They pointed to the increased traffic on the Mississippi, the removal of vegetation, the desolation of Syria and Greece, soil erosion in parts of the United States. "In the light of considerations such as these, man may well be regarded not only as a potent geological agent but as dangerously so to himself. The hope is that the intelligence that has wrought a change of surface conditions serviceable for the present, but dangerous as to the future, will be so enlarged as to inspire a still more intelligent control of surface conditions which shall compass the future welfare as well as transient benefit."[36] There was slightly over a seventy-year span between the first expressions of Lyell on the subject and these observations of Chamberlain and Salisbury.

Perhaps it is no accident that these men were American geologists, witnesses of vast changes over short periods, for what greater contrast could there be between the long history of environmental change in Europe, and the short history, motivated by the same European values, in the United States? And they wrote five years before August, 1914, the beginning of a period of wars and technological change that, in volume and magnitude of use and destruction of natural resources probably has far exceeded the total for all previous history. The United States of the nineteenth century is the best example of large-scale accelerated environmental change by man. This story has not yet been completely told, and it has been concealed rather than illumined by chapters in our histories with such titles as *The Moving Frontier* and *Winning the West.* But by 1934, the Dust Bowl storms showed, for all to see, the intimate historical relation between culture and environmental change. They began a new era in environmental studies.

Since World War II one needs a catalogue of concerns, not a list; but thought and research of all kinds have been increasingly dominated by environmental questions seen from an ecological viewpoint. Population growth, including that of huge population densities, environmental quality, and the role of ideas and values now predominate. Attitudes toward birth control have come under much closer scrutiny because they have become more and more crucial.

The acceleration of change, the increase in population, and the growing importance of values and attitudes give a prominence to the time scale in which we now look at environmental matters. In much of human history, the distinction between long-term and short-term views has not been so vital as it has now become. This, I believe, is another significant conclusion from a study of the history of ideas. Since Marsh's time many students of the modifications of the environment by man have made their pleas in favor of the long-term view. Sympathy with it is implicit in ecological thinking. It is also implicit in normative and aesthetic attitudes, in the argument for stewardship and in the concern for posterity. The long-term view requires planning, wealth, and, in this country, an infinitely greater degree of social responsibility than has yet been exhibited under the capitalistic system. The short-term view is equally real. Poor Mexican peasants cannot be expected to cease eating while efforts are made to stop the erosion of their lands. Such conditions magnify the great dilemma of growing populations on badly used lands.

XII

Nature and culture cannot be divorced from the ways men have thought about them, and their investigation may assume different forms. One can study primitive peoples' idea of space, nature in Goethe's poetry, trends in landscape painting, concepts of the land held by the Physiocrats, attitudes toward men and nature in Communist China or the history of the American conservation movement. But if we look at the nature of man, his culture and his physical environment generally, then I believe we may observe a tendency toward a gradual fusion of ideas. The condition of man forces it. This might seem strange to say in face of statements like that of

John Wild that existentialism is not concerned with nature or that in this philosophy man's "freedom to make himself separates man radically from all subhuman entities of nature," or the opening sentences of Paul Shepard's *Man in the Landscape* (1967): "To put it bluntly, said my friend, nature is out of date." By nature's being out of date he meant that the question of its relationship to man had receded, or was accorded only despair.[37]

However, we wish to express the idea—in Buffon's terms as an age in which man assists nature, as the "mental" age of Chamberlain and Salisbury in 1909, as the noosphere of Teilhard de Chardin—that it is becoming clear that the histories of culture and nature are now merging. So great is the power of mankind to change the environment that it will be unrealistic to study one without the other. Cultural mosaics vary, but the human imprint is everywhere. This fusion will place a higher premium than ever before in the past on values and attitudes because they are determinants of inertia and of change; the long history of thought attests to their importance in the past, but in an increasingly constricted world their role becomes more crucial. Man and his environment are inseparable; the care and preservation of the environment are indispensable to the survival of the human race. We are forced into a grand anthropocentrism in spite of ourselves. If the history of thought is any guide, these values will not come from any one source, but from the whole range of human thought. In the past they have come from such varied sources as science, philosophy, religion, literature, and art. Few students of contemporary trends or of the history of ideas concerning man and nature today would conceive of solutions simplistically as problems of technology and science, or of technology correcting the errors of technology.

Before our present industrial and technological age, populations were fewer and, equally important, less dense; the massive contrasts between city and country did not exist, technologies were less accelerative in their effects, and the great traditional modifiers of the earth, even the potentially deadly ones like fire and deforestation, were slower and more gradual in their cumulative effects. It is plain, too, that whatever else the word civilization means, it is not synonymous with rationality, wise use, and planning. We can no longer find solace in the Victorian contrasts between civilized man and the savage, for the opportunities for irrational behavior in civilized societies have been enormously magnified.

XIII

These long-term historical trends, and the ideas they have spawned, have forced and will continue to force an intense examination of values, and their economic, social, ethical presuppositions. A whole new literature, increasingy self-conscious and normative, about man and his environment is coming into being. It reminds one of the tremendous effort which we know as the Romantic Movement, still so controversial, still with so many friends and foes, which was made before the French Revolution and during and after the Napoleonic wars to interpret, retain, and create values whether they concerned folk art, cultural differences, wilderness, communion with nature or ruins. Perhaps, indeed, we should date the modern effort from it.

In this essay, I have tried to point out what to me are significant landmarks in Western attitudes toward nature since the end of the eighteenth century: widespread interest in the subjective aspects of nature and its evocative power so characteristic of the last part of the eighteenth and the early part of the nineteenth century; growing awareness of the force of human agency in modifying the face of the earth; the achievement of a new concept of nature, an outgrowth of the Darwinian theory; the creation of unique industrial landscapes and the re-appraisals which they have brought about. We can say that this period, up to the present, has been a period of exploration of the implications of the uniqueness of man. In its continuing exploration lies the greatest possibilities for an enlightened anthropocentrism and for a cohesive organizing principle. It could rescue us from a narrow utilitarianism, and put in different perspective the immense creative powers of man. Or, if we prefer, we can say that we should explore to the fullest man's place in nature—an old and famous phrase.

When, in the fifth century, St. Augustine wrote in the *City of God* of man's place in nature, he referred to man's position in a divine hierarchy, created by God, in which those having life are ranked above those which do not have it; those who have the power of generation or desire for it are above those lacking it. Among living things, those that are sentient are above those that are not, as animals are above trees. And among the sentient, the intelligent are above those lacking it, and among the intelligent, immortal angels are above mortal man.[38] When T.H. Huxley, in the nineteenth century, wrote of man and nature, he was concerned with man's place in an evolutionary scale, with man as a product of evolution from simpler forms of life. When we use the phrase, man's place in nature, we mean neither of these, for we are living neither in the age of St. Augustine nor of T.H. Huxley. Today, it means the place of human cultures in the natural world; it has to do with attitudes toward all of life and its environment, attitudes which are germinating in new seed beds in which the value of life and of nature must be seen against the now almost limitless obliterative capacities of man, at least on this earth. It is this last consideration that is forcing us into new formulations and that most decisively sets us apart from the past.

NOTES

1. *La Vision du passé* (Paris: Editions du Seuil, 1957), p. 349 ("Evolution de l'idée d'évolution," 1950).
2. For a discussion of this subject, see Glacken, *Traces on the Rhodian Shore. Nature and Culture from Classical Times to the End of the Eighteenth Century* (Berkeley and Los Angeles: University of California Press, 1967), chapters 3, 7, 10, 14.
3. Bk. X, viii, 7–8. Rackham trans. in the Loeb Classical Library.
4. On this point, see *Traces on the Rhodian Shore,* p. 548.
5. Leo Marx, *The Machine in the Garden. Technology and the Pastoral Ideal in America* (New York: Oxford University Press, 1964), p. 220.
6. *Kosmos. Entwurf einer physischen Weltbeschreibung.* 5 vols. (Stuttgart und Tübingen: Cotta, 1847), Vol. II, pp. 66–67.
7. On Buffon, see *Traces on the Rhodian Shore,* chap. 14.
8. *Theory of Earth, with Proofs and Illustrations.* 3 vols. (Edinburgh: W. Creech, 1795-1899). On the earth made for man, Vol. I, p. 18, 183; Vol. II, pp. 90f, 257f; man as contemplator, Vol. I, p. 167, 183; Vol. II, p. 93, 239. The whole work is concerned with processes, but see esp. Vol. II, chap 6.
9. *The Phenomenon of Man* (New York: Harper Torchbooks, the Cloister Library, New York 1961), pp. 180–183. See also Julian Huxley's remarks in his introduction to the work, note 7 above and the introduction to Buffon's *Epoques de la nature* (1778).
10. *Principles of Geology* (London: J. Murray, 1830–33), Vol. I, pp. 76–78, 154–156.
11. *Ibid.,* Vol. II, pp. 202–208.
12. *Ibid.,* Vol. I, p. 162.
13. *Ibid.,* Vol. II, pp. 82–86, 121.
14. *Ibid.,* Vol. II, pp. 147–148.
15. *Ibid.,* Vol. II, pp. 155–156.
16. *Ibid.,* Vol. II, p. 207.
17. *The Origin of Species.* Variorum text ed. by Morse Peckham (Philadelphia: University of Pennsylvania Press, 1959), chap. 3, sent. 115–123.
18. J. Arthur Thomson, *Darwinism and Human Life* (New York: Henry Holt, London: Andrew Melrose, 1910), pp. 46–47.
19. On this see *Traces on the Rhodian Shore,* chap. 8.
20. See *The Origin of Species,* as cited in n. 17 above, chap. 1 on

domestication; ch. 3 on Scotch fir and the cats-to-clover chain.
21. *A Second Visit to the United States of North America,* 2 vols. (London: J. Murray), Vol. II, pp. 23–25. *Man and Nature,* ed. by David Lowenthal (Cambridge: Belknap Press of Harvard University Press, 1965), p. xxii, Lyell to Marsh, September 22, 1865.
22. *Traces on the Rhodian Shore,* pp. 698–702.
23. *Ibid.,* pp. 489–491.
24. *The City in History* (New York: Harcourt, Brace and World, 1961), pp. 474–481 and entire chap. 15.
25. *The Works of John Ruskin ed. by E.T. Cook* and *Alexander Wedderburn.* Library ed., 39 vols. (London: G. Allen; New York, Longmans, Green, and Co., 1903–1912), Vol. IV, p. xlviii, 28–30, 143–149; VI, pp. 117–127.
26. Vol. III, p. 627n; V, pp. 323–325; VII, pp. 422–423.
27. Vol. IV, p. 31.
28. Vol VI, pp. 455–457.
29. Vol. VI, pp. 409–411.
30. Vol. V, pp. 370, 380–381.
31. Vol. VI, p. xxiv, 388–389 and chap. 19 entire.
32. Vol. VIII, pp. 190–191; IX, p. 411.
33. E.g., Vol. XXXIV, *Arrows of the Chace.*
34. Vol. XVII, p. xlii, May 16, 1863.
35. See the pref. to the 2nd ed. of Wordsworth's *Lyrical Ballads* (1800) and Kipling's *The Day's Work* (1898): "The Bridge-Builders," and ".007." See also Herbert L. Sussman, *Victorians and the Machine. The Literary Response to Technology* (Cambridge: Harvard University Press, 1968).
36. Thomas C. Chamberlain and Rollin D. Salisbury, *Geology* (New York: Henry Holt, c. 1904–06), pp. 619–620.
37. John Wild, *The Challenge of Existentialism* (Bloomington: Indiana University Press, 1959), p. 77 and Paul Shepard, *Man in the Landscape* (New York: Knopf, 1967), p. xiii.
38. *City of God,* Bk. XI, chap. 16.

BIBLICAL ROOTS OF AN ECOLOGIC CONSCIENCE

by Dr. Conrad Bonifazi

Under the increasing pressure of man's ability to change his environment, Dr. Glacken notes in the previous chapter a tendency toward the gradual fusion of ideas about human nature, culture, and our physical surroundings. He suggests that this trend, which must be viewed against man's destructive capacity, places a higher premium than hitherto upon our values and attitudes, not only because they are strong determinants of change but also because their role becomes more crucial in a growingly constricted world.

While the judgment that the care of the earth is indispensable to the survival of mankind must draw its nourishment from the entire range of human thought, the present essay examines some of its Biblical roots in recognition of their tragic neglect and hope of their stimulus and growth; in so doing it bears out Dr. Glacken's conviction that the relationship of man to the earth will continue to force an examination of values and their ethical presuppositions.

In a stirring article, "The Historical Roots of Our Ecologic Crisis,"[1] Professor Lynn White, Jr., looks beyond the alarming symptoms of our exploitive attitude toward the earth in the belief that what people do about their environment depends upon what they think of themselves: "Human ecology is deeply conditioned by beliefs about our nature and destiny—that is, by religion." He takes to task historic Christianity, especially the Western branch of the church, whose victory over paganism, he considers, to have been "the greatest psychic revolution in the history of our culture". In contrast with the creation stories of Greco-Roman mythology, he sees the Judaeo-Christian account of creation reflecting an extremely anthropocentric religion in which human beings stand over against their natural environment, all the constituents of which are planned for their benefit, so that no item in the physical creation has any purpose except to serve mankind.

Among the common people of the ancient world, animistic views were widespread. Natural objects possessed guardian spirits whom men consulted out of respect and fear before entering their domains or utilizing their resources. But, by destroying pagan animism, Christianity made it possible to exploit nature in a mood of indifference to natural objects. Against the pagan assumption that spirit dwelt in nature, Christianity was able to assert man's effective monopoly of spirit in this world, and, inasmuch as the old inhibitions to nature's exploitation crumbled, the earth lay defenseless and at the mercy of men.

Added to this in the Latin West, the religious study of nature as revealing the mind of God did not remain a symbolic system through which God was understood to speak; instead, natural theology became a genuine effort to understand God's mind by discovering how his creation worked. It could, therefore, be said that modern science began as an outgrowth of natural theology, while technology expressed practically the Christian dogma of man's rightful mastery over nature.

Professor Lynn White pays fine and proper tribute to the humble saint of Assisi who sought to depose men's imperialistic attitude to nature by regarding himself as one member of the familial assembly of all God's creatures. But St. Francis was a notable exception, whose efforts failed in this respect, for technology and science today are "so tinctured with orthodox Christian arrogance toward nature that no solution for our ecologic crisis can be expected from them alone." And, despite the fact that the roots of the crisis are so largely religious and need a religious remedy, orthodox Christianity, with its stress upon the spiritual autonomy of man over against the material facts of nature, cannot address itself to the problem with any hope of success. A significant growing point of an ecologic conscience, however, may well be contained in the early Franciscan sense of the "spiritual autonomy of all parts of nature".

This is Professor Lynn White's argument. That its thrust reflects a major emphasis of the Christian religion throughout the centuries cannot be genuinely contradicted. It is true that in the interests of spiritual religion Christianity has regarded the natural world as an enemy; failing to recognize that the *unnatural* might be antithetical to the natural, it set nature in opposition to grace, and in pursuit of the community of man as its religious ideal, permitted his natural environment to fall into discredit.

If the authors of *This Little Planet* conceive of their corporate task as an attempt to reinstate the concept of the natural, the purpose of this chapter is to oppose the momentum of orthodox Christianity in its devaluation of the natural world, and to show that in so doing it has been untrue to its own literary and cultural sources, which are finally concentrated and disclosed in the "Word made flesh." The religion of the *incarnate* Word was all too quickly attacked by an ascetic virus which undermined its natural elements in favor of the supernatural. This atrophy of interest in the natural makes nonsense of the whole concept of Incarnation whereby the

New Testament wished to affirm that the God who is personal Love is indissolubly united not only with the human race but also with the entire universe of matter.

So, before abandoning hope in the Christian religion as a source of the renewal of the earth, this essay examines briefly the literary sources and original inspiration of Christianity in the belief that valuable roots for the transignification* of the natural world are embedded, and still nourish themselves, there.

In modern times the despoilment of the earth accompanies our appreciation of natural beauty, but a sense of earth's beauty has stimulated the imagination of cultures other than our own. The Hebrew conception of the natural world not only provides color and material for narrative but also shapes the imagery and inspires the vocabulary of the Bible. The love lyrics of the Song of Solomon, to take a notable example, are couched in descriptions of natural beauty, and the human qualities of the lovers themselves are presented in terms of plants, animals, trees, perfumes, birds, precious stones and metal, architecture and contours of the landscape.[2] This aesthetic appreciation of nature envelops a sense of wonder before the mystery and incomprehensibility of the earth, the forces which sustain it, the limits of the cloud-wrapped ocean, the functions and behavior of soil and water, the dimensions of Earth and the movements of celestial bodies. The intricacy of nature, the habits of animals and birds, and the wisdom portrayed in their survival evoke the same *mysterium tremendum.*[3]

But Hebrews, like other men, could not permanently live with the nonrational and mysterious without visualizing for themselves a rational order in things. While the psalmist pro-

*See page 225

vides us with a picture of nature as a going concern,[4] it was given to a prophet to instruct us clearly in the sociology of the natural world:

> *I will answer the heavens,*
> *And they shall answer the earth;*
> *And the earth shall answer the grain, the wine and the oil;*
> *And they shall answer Jezreel.*[5]

This ordered world of interrelated creatures and things is not held together for the Hebrews by "natural law," but is animated, ruled, and sustained by the "breath of God." And when we turn from the phenomenological aspects of existence to the inwardness of things, and from the immediate, sensory impact of environment to consider what people thought about the material world, the Biblical writers display an awareness of its nature which even at this distance from them we may come to consider worthy of helping to refashion our own more dangerous relations with things. For they regarded the earth as alive, and acknowledged no fundamental distinction between the psychic and the corporeal, or between what we choose to call the "organic" and the "inorganic." Everything is a manifestation of life; the earth has its nature, makes itself felt, and demands respect; the very stones are alive; death is not antithetical to life, it is the weakest form of life.

This attitude has been thought, perhaps hastily, to embody a "pre-logical mentality," yet Old Testament writers have no difficulty in distinguishing between the physical and metaphysical aspects of existence; but they believed in a unity of life which allowed of no separation between the material and the spiritual as *fundamental* forms of existence. For them, soul and body are not united, for they were never apart: body *is* soul in its outwardness, and soul *is* body in its inwardness.

The total personality is operative in any one aspect or part of the whole, so that various parts of the body comprise psychical as well as physical properties; that is to say: man's consciousness is diffused throughout his person. The condition of the psalmist's life may be tested by the state of his kidneys[6] and Job's palate may pronounce upon perversity.[7]

> *Who hath put wisdom in the inward parts?*
> *Or who hath given understanding to the heart?*[8]

In contrast, therefore, with the mental habit which dissociates ideas from things, the Hebrews found it more natural to think descriptively and pictorially, linking firmly with ideas the objects, movements, and sensory data of their environment. And, unlike our predominant habit of analysis, of breaking up wholes into parts, they envisaged phenomena as participating in wholes. Man himself is thinking and feeling flesh, blood, and bone. Stating their view in our terms, we might say that a man is insouled body and enfleshed soul, except that the Hebrew word *nephesh,* often translated "soul" and represented here by "a man," does not carry the fractional connotation which "soul" bears in our minds on account of its association and contrast with "body." *Nephesh* frequently expresses "life," but again without bearing the abstract sense which may lie hidden in our use of the word. The psalmist's cry for deliverance of soul is a spontaneous prayer that he himself be saved from death.[9]

Phrases describing the soul's departure at death and its return at life's renewal must not be understood as the severance of soul from body, but rather as a diminishing or a revival of man's total human life; for a soul may be nourished physically and survive, while the dead are still "the weak." A corpse is a soul, "living and partly living."

So, because the Hebrews understood consciousness to be distributed throughout the body, it was possible to conceive of psychical qualities in the natural world. After all, our bodies are the one part of nature of which we have an inside view, and the body seemed to show how nature felt and acted when viewed from within. It seemed natural to extend this awareness to the external world, to regard one's environment anthropomorphically, as thoroughly animated, capable both of fellow-feeling with human beings and of obedience to its own sustaining depth of force.

Therefore, *nephesh* is not peculiarly human; there is no ultimate division between human and animal *nephesh;* indeed, life and sensibility extend through the animal kingdom into the world of objects. Perhaps because their volatile contents, perfume bottles are "houses of the soul,"[10] and if mountains shake or trees "clap their hands," these personal propensities of a glad earth are more than poetry; they betoken an intricate connection between man and the earth, understood by analogy. The relationship between them, however, may properly be described as *living* because men visualized their surroundings as sharing in their own psychic nature.

This basic view of man and nature can be stated in another way by saying that in Israelite understanding a man's individuality does not stop short at his physical exterior; his personality, unbounded by his bodily presence, extends into other persons and things which would be regarded by the analytical mind as separate from him. A man's vital power bears not only the marks of his own character but embraces also his relatives and his property. If men are to be put to death, their immediate relatives and possessions perish with them;[11] yet this apparently wholesale carnage, on the understanding of extended personality, is not, unfortunately, without its raison d'être.

More positively and generally stated, the Hebrews regarded nothing as lifeless in itself; all is susceptible to the force and content of *nephesh.* Objects share the qualities of their possessors, so that to make a gift is to give something of oneself.

The living earth is intimately connected with its inhabitants, whose personal life is reflected in the conditions of the impressionable soil and the forms of life it sustains. Earth's relationship to men is not that of a dead mass to living beings; the earth is partner in a covenant relationship which is not invariably dominated from the human side. The positive strength of life, the power to thrive and accomplish one's task is called "blessing," while its opposite, "the curse," spells dissolution of soul. The land shares man's blessing and curse, responding bounteously to strength and kindness, but not suffering exhaustion without giving the appearance of a wilderness. And when, at seven-yearly intervals, its life became inviolate, this was not that it might lie fallow, but become free, a no-man's-land pursuing its own nature. Man and earth are a psychic community; they are the constituents of personal life.[12]

The most immediate extension of *nephesh* occurs by word of mouth, and the close connection between "soul" and that which is affected by it presupposes the power of the word: a force not wholly material as though a spoken word were a missile launched into its environment, nor yet an undifferentiated quantum of energy, but essentially powerful in a milieu capable of response by virtue of the same basic soul-quality.

Nephesh is characterized by its "fleshy" constituent (*basar*); it is not in itself an ontological substance, but has its reality in localized, material, corporeal being. In human beings it does not operate with uniform strength, but depends upon the occasion and degree to which a man puts his heart into what he does and says. His name is the immediate bearer of his *nephesh:* his words of blessing augment life; his curses undo it. For when his *nephesh* is a totality which extends and moves out into space, thinking is not separate from speaking, nor speaking from doing. Images of the memory press toward action; and words, in order to escape vanity, issue in events.

Thinking is not pure theory, nor is knowledge mere recognition. Concrete problems require more than abstract solutions, and yield only to those answers whose shape is association and action.

This relationship of inwardness to outwardness is characterized in the Hebrew language by the absence of a word to represent a material thing. Things are sometimes referred to as means of action or as objects of desire, but these designations still bear the marks of human preference and motive. For the Hebrews, *a thing is principally a word, dabhar.* In our language a *thing* means any action, speech, or thought with which we are concerned; it is any object of perception or knowledge; it is both idea and event. But our sense of the discontinuity between thinking and doing makes us judge this usage to be ambiguous. The Old Testament finds no ambiguity here; idea, word, and event are a continuous whole. Abraham's returning servant recounts "all the words he had done."[13] His adventurous journey in its entirety is comprised of words! Things are not objects in space; they are words. Things are not inflexibly but only changeably *there,* because they are directly and continuously related to mankind. Descriptions of the earth in terms of motion and energy, the skipping mountains and their trembling foundations, are more than poetic images of seismic phenomena; they express a lively earth related to living men. And *dabhar,* a word, comprises all: thoughts, words, deeds, and concrete objects, so that nothingness or non-being is stated as that which is *not-word, lo-dabhar.* Between these extremes, couched within the unity of word and deed, lay a sense of counterfeit language. People recognized the word which lacked the strength for its own fulfillment; but the effective word could create or destroy in accordance with its character.

So the liveliness of *nephesh* becomes *dabhar;* strength and quality of "soul" pass into speech and action; the energy of *nephesh* is articulate; it carries the notion of being behind and pressing forward, and so, perhaps, of pressing words one after another into existence. In the realm of speech, *dabhar* easily relates to "the idea behind it"; in the world of action, it is bound up with those forces and circumstances of which the event is a culmination. Events germinate in background words!

Dabhar, then, a word, contains and unfolds the essence of things; and when it appears in Greek dress as *logos* (in the Septuagint) the Greek heritage tends to heighten the intelligibility of *dabhar* without, however, staunching its Semitic flow of energy. For the *logos* of the Greeks recognized speech as the critical arrangement of words; it stressed the content of speech rather than actual speaking; and eventually bore responsibility for conveying the Greek supposition that within and throughout the world dwelt a norm assisting men to self-understanding in their cosmic environment. So, broadly speaking, we may say that by *logos* the Greeks emphasized the articulate element of *dabhar* to complement its energetic principle which moved Hebrew consciousness more profoundly.

It is fascinating to note the development in Judaeo-Christian scripture of this "word-character" of existence. In the prophetic tradition of Israel, the word which appeared as vision and action, and was expressed in poetry, prose, and pun, and was understood to be an outpouring of the life of the speaker, acquired still deeper significance. The prophet became the spokesman of Yahweh whose words were placed in his mouth[14] to engage in the creativity and destructiveness of the Lord. Prophetic utterances bore the hallmark of their origin, "Thus saith Yahweh"; and collections of oracles were introduced as "the word of the Lord." Thus the relationship of the prophet to his word became enveloped within a larger whole, and the word which rested upon the prophet's personal relation to Yahweh now becomes the word of Yahweh himself,[15] and the prophet becomes the extended personality of God.

This movement in which the mystery of being unfolds itself in Israel is not confined to the prophets, but has its counterparts in the priestly and humanist traditions. Priests are mediators of the Law, which also is a word:

> for out of Zion shall go forth the law, and the
> word of the Lord from Jerusalem.[16]

Torah, or teaching about God, inherits more than documentary status and is regarded as a power nucleus with wider applicability in time and space than any one particular prophetic utterance. The *Ten Words* of covenantal significance do not need to be retrieved from far-flung hiding places, for they are also in people's mouths and hearts to be fulfilled, or to destroy their possessors with the bone-burning fever of their unspokenness.[17] The interchangeability of *Torah* with *dabhar* in Psalm 119 says that the dianoetic quality of the one mingles with the dynamic force of the other. Once creativity and the force of life reverberate in *Torah* and *dabhar* alike, both participate in shaping and sustaining the world. By the word of Yahweh were the heavens made; the first-begotten *Torah,* agent of the world's formation, lights up primeval darkness and spells out life everywhere.

The wisdom literature of the humanists in Israel was dominated by a godly fear so practical as to concern itself with men's skills and their conduct of daily affairs. Such wisdom was highly prized, and some men ranked it as being present at the world's formation. This feeling is expressed in the Book of Proverbs, where wisdom (*hochmah*), feminine and personal, speaks for herself:

> *Yahweh possessed me in the beginning of his way, before his works of old.*
>
> *I was set up from everlasting, from the beginning, or ever the earth was.*
>
> *When there were no depths I was brought forth; when there were no fountains abounding with water.*
>
> *Before the mountains were settled, before the hills was I brought forth:*
>
> *While as yet he had not made the earth, nor the fields, nor the highest part of the dust of the world.*
>
> *When he prepared the heavens I was there: when he set a vault upon the face of the deep . . .*
>
> *Then I was by him, as one brought up with him; and I was daily his delight, rejoicing always before him.*[18]

The origins of *dabhar, Torah,* and *hochmah* may remain obscure, but their confluence attains a further depth when apprehended in the personal Logos whom men subsequently identify with the historical Jesus.

> That which was from the beginning, which we have heard, which we have seen with our eyes, which we have looked upon, and our hands have handled, of the Word of life . . .[19]

The vital energy which imbued matter, the soul which spoke within and from the material world with human accents is now articulately "full of grace and truth." The sublimity and unconscious power of the world achieve emotional intensity, are "made flesh," and the hitherto inaccessible depths of the material world acquire lucidity. The mercurial essence of matter under sensory observation and the illusory dimensions of its mysterious façade have been penetrated and "divined."

The Hebrews, it seems, were not enamored of world-reason, and their messianic expectancy did not focus attention beyond the human, but their sight, hearing, and touch of Jesus pressed them to heap upon him those qualities which hitherto had been invested only in the Word of prophecy, the Law, and in Wisdom herself. Their earlier values are neither dismissed nor annulled, but serve a personal category in which they are fulfilled. The new affirmation of the nature of the world is not an enlarged concept but a living person. The person is not a traditionalist but one in whom all received values are present in a new way to confirm the personal nature of things, and who crowns with life the concept of the inwardness and the outwardness of matter. The heart of the energy which is the world, and the content of all that had gone before, now become tangibly and lovingly present. The vast multiplicity of things, hitherto dumb or relatively inarticulate, are now sensitively and intelligently articulated in him; he is the essence of their implicit power, and the concretion of "matter" and "spirit." All things are summarized in him, for "all that came to be was alive with his life."[20] The Word which was "made flesh" constitutes, then, the Christian awareness of the nature of things and the category by which creation is understood and appraised.

If Jesus as Logos manifests the *nature* of man and the world, we must consider now the Biblical concept of their *destiny.*

A decisive influence upon the Hebrew sense of destiny was exerted by the view that soul and body are the inwardness and outwardness of a man, and that each person extends beyond his physique to embrace his family and to penetrate his property. His well-being or salvation included the extensions of his personality, so that deliverance for the whole man meant deliverance from every kind of ill. His religion strongly affirmed this world, and was conceived of practically as responsibility for communal existence here and now, without promise of a transcendental destiny for the "soul." (A study of the development of the doctrine of the Resurrection in the Old Testament reveals only faint and intermittent hope of bodily revivification!)

However, in joy of deliverance from slavery, and fear of the antagonisms of life, the Hebrews became engaged in a covenant with Yahweh. And if we say that this covenant involved the blessing of Yahweh and the obedience of Israel, God's protection and his people's service, its contractual appearance must not obscure the permanent, personal relationship between them; they were bound together by "steadfast love." But once a community has entered upon a covenant promising conditional well-being, the impact of political and natural environment offers a tremendous challenge to its faith. In face of hunger, poverty, homelessness, and humiliation, it would be possible for some men to abandon the practical aspects of their faith, and rather than watch it founder in a sea of adversity, they would maintain it by transferring the fulfillment of its promised salvation to another world.

The Hebrews did not shrink the garment of salvation by immersing it in some other-worldly reference and meaning; they allowed it to remain exposed to the turmoil of this world and sought to envelop within it the whole of their natural environment. Thus they interpreted their destiny in the broad terms of a unity of personal life with that of their surroundings, and recognized a direct relationship between disasters which appeared from physical and political sources and the transgressions of personal and national existence. For example, the prophet Amos not only envisages the political downfall of the kingdom of Israel but asks its inhabitants to interpret adverse physical phenomena such as drought and blight as auguries of an all-inclusive judgment upon their way of life.[21] And although the relationship between men and the earth is expressed in terms of destruction rather than well-being, so that words of comfort contained in prophetic utterances are often regarded as suspect, the fact that judgment could involve nature along with man seems to imply a corresponding unity in well-being.

On this reading of events, political nemesis overtook the Hebrews when they were swept eastward on the receding tide of Babylonian invasion. The painfulness of exile was eventually gladdened by return to their homeland, but their foreign experiences have often been judged to have forced their abandonment of any concept of salvation which included their natural environment in favor of apocalyptic hopes which left this world to its ruin. This view implies that the Hebrews reformulated the account of their destiny in order to see it in other-worldly terms, and certainly within the tangled skein of apocalyptic literature strands of pessimism are abundantly visible.

Belief in a righteous God as the prophetic tradition fostered it, helped to determine the concept of "the day of the Lord" as one of judgment upon mankind, a day of darkness rather than light. These somber predictions, however, did not drain life of its meaning, but tended rather to add dignity and seriousness to men's choices and behavior. Apocalyptic literature has this prophetic root and the leitmotifs imported into it from other sources do not eradicate its Hebrew character. Resurrection life in a new heaven and a new earth is to be lived *in the flesh;* the pessimism which conceives of this world as unfit for the realization of the Golden Age is nevertheless accompanied by the neighborly yet paradoxical optimism which anticipates its advent here.[22]

Apocalypticism has often been denied symbolic value by those who understood it to be historical prediction. Myths about the beginning of the world have revealed more of their permanent value for being divested of their "literal truth," while myths concerning the end of the world have not shared equally in this edifying dénouement; so, despite the relatedness of beginning and end, the disclosure of the character of man's destiny has not been permitted to complement that of his origin. Seeking to penetrate the broken surfaces of things, the apocalypticists declared the unity of cosmological with human events. Despairing of all finitude, they continued to find hope in the wholeness of divine purposes, so that their inability to affirm the eternity of the natural world of sensory experience did not mean that they abandoned it to destruction, but understood it rather to be included in the saving processes implied in their covenant. The Gospels reveal two strains in the teaching of Jesus: one which appears to contemplate the indefinite continuance of human life under historical conditions, and another which seems to suggest a speedy end to these conditions. Strangely enough, then, apocalyptic despair of this world is overarched by hope of a *transformation* of the whole of creation.

This hope and despair are set out in peculiar imagery. The power of things to persist both structurally and vitally in time, over against chaos and disease, is attributed to spiritual beings: the creative forces to the good, and the destructive to the evil. Christianity has understood its founder to have mastered the powers of this demonic world, though the acknowledgement of his victory has sometimes been interpreted as a denial of the existence of its powers! So sweeping a denial can hardly effect more than a formal separation of man from the mysterious inner depths of natural life. The phenomena and noumena explained by spiritual presences surrounding and invading men's lives have not surely vanished from the earth, so that what was once attributed to the influences of personal or semipersonal beings is still experienced in the breakdown of individual integrity within the mass of men, or has come to be expressed in the idiom of the sciences, in the language of psychology and in the theories of heredity and determinism. The myths of spiritual beings, of "the prince of this world" and his demon entourage, symbolize what is chaotic and discordant in the structure of existence: natural catastrophe, sickness and anxiety, enmity between human beings, distress in creation and the disparate phenomena of nature; in a word—things as they are compared with that world order of which men dream and which they believe to be their destiny.

The clear, unfallen world of the beginning, the myth of paradise, bears this eschatological connotation. Our human condition is set within a framework of destiny. Our actuality is a becoming. And our *implicit* destiny in the myth of the fall, with its ramifications in the natural world, is spelled out in the myth of a restored paradise. This paradise motif was not obliged to await an age in which apocalyptic literature became fashionable; expressing as it did an elemental human longing, prophets and psalmists also give it forms appropriate to their literary genres. Isaiah, for example, pictures an idyllic reconciliation in which the enmity between animals of different species is superseded by peace, and the inadvertence of children among creatures normally dangerous brings no injurious effects. This peaceful order is attributed by the prophet to a world immersed in "the knowledge of the Lord."[23]

Ezekiel draws a similar picture, but extends the hope of restoration from the world of animals into the kingdom of plants, and joins the fruitful earth with man's knowledge of the Lord as a deliverer from slavery and exploitation.[24]

What these prophets contemplate does not vary in principle from the covenant at Sinai, but exceeds it cosmically in breadth of validity, so that Hosea, who also speaks about the congeniality of vegetable and animal life, grounds his symbolism in a renewed covenant of *nature* with Yahweh.[25] No doubt, an impersonal view of the essence of matter, or of the nature of the world, makes Hosea's suggestion preposterous, but the Hebrew appraisal of the earth as psychic in quality invests it with wisdom and insight.

This prophetic symbolism, enfolding the earth with the destiny of man, was later focused in the image of the Holy City, the New Jerusalem in which superfluousness of sun and moon as sources of light in face of the divine glory, suggest the overcoming of the antithesis of the natural and the divine, while the multitudinous paean of celestial praise is shared both by "living creatures" and by "every created thing in heaven and on earth and under the earth and in the sea, all that is in them."[26] This ecumenical, indeed cosmic, song bears symbolic testimony to the undiminished apocalyptic hope of nature's inclusion within the processes of salvation.

The writers of the synoptic gospels implement this Hebrew heritage in testimony to Jesus. They breathe apocalyptic air. Sensing the mysterious conception of the new earth, seminally present in Jesus, they portray him as victor over the demonic powers of the world. Those powers, which had hitherto held all nature in thrall, now lie broken; the day of the ecumenical song has dawned; men stand upon its threshold. The cosmic significance of Jesus does not yet find conceptual form, but the worlds of nature and of the spirit are one kingdom only, of which he is master. And to those who wish to perpetuate the aberrant divorcement of the two spheres, Jesus is recorded as saying:

> Is it easier to say to this paralyzed man, "Your sins are forgiven," or to say, "Stand up, take your bed, and walk"? But to convince you that the Son of Man has the right on earth to forgive sins—he turned to the paralyzed man—"I say to you, stand up, take your bed, and go home." And he got up, took his stretcher at once, and went out. . . .[27]

So what the apocalypticists had symbolically portrayed, the synoptic gospelers report as event and actuality within the dimensions of their personal experience. Renewal of the spirit and healing of the body are not unrelated movements; there is no wholeness for man without restoration for nature by virtue of their mutual enfoldment.

The directness of the Gospel reports and their comparative freedom from interpretation leave the door of memory ajar upon events, so that it is left to other New Testament writers to draw out their implications and to conceptualize the nature of the ministry Jesus performed.

St. Paul looks in this direction and views the world with eyes of apocalyptic ambiguity; his despair of the here and now contends with his hope of its restoration. His synonymous use of the phrase "this world" with "this age," and the powers or "princes" which were said to dominate it, link closely the created world with man's predicament in it, and emphasize a despair with which we then associate remarks which might describe retreat from the world, retirement into himself, and rescue of a metaphysical sort while "this world" hastens to its end. But alongside this picture of disintegration, St. Paul is aware of processes of upbuilding, and he sees a world—comprising nature and man—which is both the theater and the object of salvation.

If we conceive of ourselves as existential unities and are concerned with wholeness and deliverance from all that isolates and divides, then hope and faith must take account of our roots in nature and embrace the physical world. If we regard ourselves as essentially divisible, soul from body, then hope must fasten upon escape from the flesh and from this earth, and faith must reach out toward wholeness of a metaphysical kind.

The spiritual aristocrats of St. Paul's day felt obliged to dissociate by degrees the evil of creation from the goodness of

God; they regarded matter as the principle of evil. But the pressures of this spiritual ecology evoke from St. Paul a conceptualization of the life and passion of Jesus, whose historical achievements he sees as invested with cosmic significance. Compared with gnostic anxiety to escape the contagion of evil by dominating matter and evading its toils, St. Paul sees Jesus, by character and action, embodying the essence of the universe: Jesus represents and epitomizes, initiates and completes the nature of the world whose energies from man to the farthest star bend toward reconciliation. What had been veiled in abstraction is now unrestrictedly open to view, for the character of the universe is summed up "in Christ" through whom it has been created and moves upon its reconciliatory way.[28]

The apostle's language naturally reflects the cosmology of his time, but his words of exaltation simultaneously reveal his understanding of the essence of the world. It is this: that the abstract energies which enliven all things meet together and acquire personal features in Jesus. Everything is gathered up into him.[29] The forces of nature and history, and the elements of what has since been designated as "the phenomenal-noumenal world" are concentrated in him and shown to be personal. He is the source of universal life, its center of development and the principle of its coherence. He is the beginning and the end, the source and goal of creation; everything emerges from him and converges upon him; he is its point of emanation and its harmonious climax.

In this language the pessimism of apocalyptic expectation is held and contained within a vision of cosmic reconciliation; but, simultaneously and unavoidably, St. Paul is obliged to express a doctrine of matter which asserts that "the world is charged with the grandeur of God," a grandeur which "flames out" in Jesus. In his description of the essence of things the *word* (*logos*) is not mentioned, but the idea of the *logos* clearly informs his thinking.

With greater firmness, perhaps, the Fourth Gospel asserts that "through him all things came to be; no single thing was created without him. All that came to be was alive with his life,"[30] but it adds nothing to that which is already implicit in St. Paul's terminology. His letter to the Romans introduces an unexpected element of destiny in which he sees the physical universe involved, and, corresponding with his faith and hope for mankind, he declares that creation itself is contained within man's wholeness and will share "in the liberty and splendor of the children of God."[31] In this astounding measure the language of faith dignifies the material world and binds it to man's future.

In looking beyond these Biblical sources concerning the nature and destiny of man and the world to the emphases and interpretations given to Christian revelation by the historic church, it is not difficult to sense the cogency of Professor Lynn White's criticisms. Broadly speaking, Christianity in the West tended to be centered upon freeing the individual from his burden of sin, and in the East, though retaining there a vision of cosmic redemption, upon the transfusion of the life of the Christian with the life of God. In practice, the church has not been concerned with the liberation and development of the natural world; and, from the second to the fifth centuries particularly, it radically perverted the spirit of the New Testament in its regard for matter. During that time, despite the war waged by Christianity against Iranian dualism, Manichaeism seeped through the Gnostics into the Christian body, and, instead of remaining an indispensable vehicle of spirit, matter came to be regarded as a drag upon it!

But in response to Professor White's acknowledgement of our need to "find a new religion or to rethink our old one," this present sketch of the Biblical sources of Christianity is drawn in the belief that these sources may still prove capable of nourishing an ecologic conscience. If the witness of animism to the sacredness of nature was deprived of its power by Judaeo-Christian religion, and the spirits in natural objects which protected them from man were forced to disappear, the Biblical testimony to the essence of things affirms that "divinity plunged into matter" in order to redeem it. Only when the cosmic significance of Incarnation was lost to view could Christianity regard the world as a neutral medium or endorse its exploitation. That "the Word was made flesh" came to be regarded primarily as undergirding man's "spiritual" existence, but it affirms both his roots in matter and the *personal* nature of the world. "Through your own incarnation, my God, all matter is henceforth incarnate."[32] We live in a divine milieu.

This evaluation of matter is brought into sharpest focus by Jesus, who refers to a piece of bread as his body. In consequence of this, the church set at the heart of its worship small elements of matter which have never ceased to give offense; for the importance granted by the church to spirit at the expense of matter had the effect of turning this moment of revelation into one of division and strife. In the mystery of the Holy Mass the religious emphasis falls upon concepts of offering and sacrifice: the presentation of bread and wine upon the altar is understood as the offering-up of Jesus Christ to God and the involvement of the worshippers in this sacrifice. But when it is said that "Christ is present at the august sacrifice of the altar ... above all under the eucharistic species" and that the Eucharist "contains in a permanent manner the Author of grace Himself,"[33] this ascription to matter of the reality of Christ reflects an authentic Biblical understanding of the nature of the world. Crude contrasts between body and soul, false antitheses of spirit and matter as good and evil have obstructed the church's vision so that it failed to recognize in the enactment of its profoundest moment of truth the transignification* of *all* matter and the declaration of the *earth* as holy.

The design arguments of physical theology in conjunction with the doctrine of the love of God for mankind in Jesus Christ facilitated the assumption that God had actually planned creation for man's benefit and that the raison d'être of the physical world was to serve human well-being. The picture of the world dominated by man was also linked with a view of God who, in turn, was conceived of as the Sovereign King of creation, exterior to it, and simultaneously its author.

*A fuller explanation of the term 'transignification' is given by the Roman Catholic scholar, Edward Schillebeeckx, O.P., in his book, *The Eucharist* (London: Sheed and Ward, Stagbooks, 1968) pp.144–151, in a section entitled, Transubstantiation and Transsignification or a New Giving of Meaning. This latter term must surely come to occupy some, if not all, of the space hitherto held by 'transubstantiation', and for the following reasons.

Inasmuch as we cannot conceive of matter without ascribing to it some qualities of mind, nor of mind without according to it some qualities of matter, "change of substance" is too objective and needs to be modified by a "new giving of meaning". The sensory data stimulated by our surroundings cannot be regarded as objective qualifications of reality, for they are not simply attributes of a "substance" which is, so to speak, situated at some deeper level. For example, the solar system in its thingliness is no doubt prior to man, but it is he who gives it meaning in order to make for himself a human world. Our human condition determines the way in which reality appears, though what in fact shows itself to us does also act as a norm for the meaning we give to it. Reality is *not behind* the appearances; the appearances are the reality itself; they are the world plus the meaning-giving presence and action of men, open to fresh discovery and disclosure. In an evolutive world there is a sense in which "transubstantiation" takes place, but as an *underlying* substance is no longer credible and we recognize that the world changes with us, that it acquires new meanings as we enter into new relationships with it, we are led to say that it is trans-signified rather than transsubstantiated.

Consequently the rapport between this Ruler and his creation was of the order which exists between an object and the one who makes it, except for one thing: because of some inexplicable mischief, the object was found to be distorted and had deteriorated in such a way as to make its use most difficult.

In this view, God, man, and the world were reciprocally alienated, but the alienation of the world bore no significance. The world as matter had no particular meaning; it became the background for a drama of sin and redemption without participating in the ontic reality of man, and was eventually discounted in favor of Paradise! When, in contrast with this, the doctrine of Incarnation is permitted to describe God's relationship with the world, we have to state that God does not reign from outside over a world structurally strange to him; *he rules over the world by assuming it.*

If, then, we follow the general Christian intention of abiding by the person and work of Jesus as central and decisive in directing us toward the realities of our human situation in respect to God and the world, it is shattering to contrast the Biblical notion of dominion with the opportunism of those who interpreted the Genesis mandate to "have dominion . . . over all the earth"[34] as man's license to exploit his natural environment. For the authority of Jesus and the understanding of his dominion grow out of his availability and service to men, expressed in patterns of caring and compassion which eventually qualify his "dominion over all the earth." As a master at knowing what it meant to be in other men's shoes, the desperate condition of his contemporaries entered through this openness into him; he made their misery his own affair. His compassion did not rob men of their destiny—as though pain were not an accompaniment of love, or death were not a creative force—but men drew strength and hope from this immeasurably great and courageous young man into whose life and personal destiny their own forlorn condition had been gathered and, there within him, was being changed. And this sympathy, nourished by passionate belief in a future close at hand, indeed already within men, constitutes his "lordship" over creation.

We may say, then, that Biblical dominion does not masquerade in the vesture of servility in order to exert a false power over the world; it breathes humility, "lording it" over none. And, inasmuch as the death of Jesus is a culmination of his life, in the sense that the life interprets the death, his ultimate authority springs from the somber glory of his cross, which, from the depths of existence, raises to dignity mankind and the world.

Here then, for the Christian man, in the doctrine of Incarnation, appear the qualities and characteristics of the creative presence of God in the world, the mechanics of creativity, and clues to man's deportment on the earth. But how shall we interpret this in the world of today?

The proverbial stagnation of Oriental peoples was attributable in part to their understanding of the sacredness of nature. Its desacralization among Occidental men released forces of inquiry which have not ceased to drive us along ways of scientific advancement, so that immense technological structures now rest upon a "secular" view of the world which has become a field of exploration and endeavor from which the gods have supposedly been excluded. All the consequences of the secularizing of nature have not yet reached fruition; that matter may be utilized without consideration for the fate of mankind and the earth as a whole is seen to be fraught with extreme hazard. Nature had to be disenchanted in order to advance the humanization of man and his physical environment, for the technical use of nature is also a revelation of its mystery. But what is called "secular" cannot be a "godless" part of life. It is rather the matter-of-factness of everything alienated *by man* from its own virtue and bounty; it is the potentially holy awaiting "the revealing of the sons of God,"[35] and suffering meanwhile eclipse and frustration till men shall see their own destinies wedded to that of the world.

The Biblical category of the *Word* is one in which matter may be described as the outwardness of spirit, and spirit as the inwardness of matter. It disregards the external world as an abstract entity satisfactorily defined by science and philosophy, and bestows upon man and nature together a personal meaning and destiny. This is what Christian orthodoxy had hidden from us and what evolution has disclosed in its own way: namely, that we are of the world, and that the ontology of man depends upon a general ontology which includes matter. So, from its relegation to mere background for a drama of salvation, through the instrumentality of Biblical and evolutionary thinking, matter is promoted to the role of the propelling force of reality. *We are* this matter which constitutes the fabric of the universe; the world is our way of being; the earth is man and cannot remain something which men examine merely from outside; it must become that within which men examine themselves.

The category of the *word* refuses to deal with the world as it reacts to cold scientific prodding, but prods man himself, seeking to focus and deepen his human response to the family of man and the world as a whole. It is a beam of light searching man's inwardness; its disclosures of his nature and destiny penetrate simultaneously the opaqueness of the world whose structures it would illuminate from within and show us "a new creation."[36] And, though the *Word* does not finally yield to rational analysis, it does invade the realm of rationality by nourishing a logic of survival, for it does not wish the atom to catch fire or history to end in the triumph of reason and the agony of mankind.

This Biblical view of man and the world must be seen and must stand in its own light, and be judged by its ability or inability to augment life and to humanize the world.

At least since the appearance of man upon earth there can have been no *absolute* nature, no untouched natural environment, but only the world interspersed with men's artifices and in process of humanization. We are so interlocked with our physical surroundings that even our explanations of them transform them. The entire assemblage of energies, creatures and things which make up our sensible world constantly interacts with us and is never unambiguous of meaning. Simone Weil contrasts a mother sewing a layette for her unborn child with a female convict in a prison workshop who is also sewing. The attention of both women is absorbed by similar technical problems, while "a whole gulf of difference" lies within their occupational similiarities.[37] Matter may weigh us down or uphold us, degrade of ennoble, threaten life or sustain it, become a source of weariness or exuberance; but its "nature" and effects will be determined by our relationship with it.

Through a personal universe, one may have to tread with unaccustomed delicacy and humility, but it will not suffice for human beings to conform to nature because they regard it as unalterable by virtue of its sacredness. To overadapt oneself to the world is to succumb to the limitations of things, while mere reaction to the provocation of environment by exploiting or subjecting it to a master-slave relationship is a dialectic of descent toward the subhuman. In a personal universe our affinity with things does not permit us to enjoy freedom without according freedom to matter. If material things cannot be liberated from man's parasitic interest and stupid infatuation, and from the frenzy of his accelerating productivity, he himself shall not taste freedom. A personal universe demands that we treat the world in such a way that our thinking about it and our handling of it release within us the power of becoming human, and elevate the status of things themselves through the treatment they receive.

Those questions posit a false antithesis, therefore, which ask whether the Biblical restoration of all things is to be regarded as "subjective" or "objective"; whether the rehabilitation of which the Bible speaks will be accounted for by our changed perceptions and attitudes of mind, or accomplished irrespective of men. Our relation to the natural world is not of a purely external character. It is a dialectic of exchange and ascension. The proclamation that "the Word became flesh," of which the eucharistic symbols are crowning instances and paradigms, affirms this ascensional force of the world in which matter is charged with the dimensions of Christ and shares in the power which reconciles, or (to speak in a world of becoming) the power which holds all things in creative tension. The bright strand of cosmic redemption drawn through Biblical literature not only indicates an affinity and destiny common to man and the world, but also attributes to matter as to man a function within the salvation structures it describes. It shows nature participating with man in the processes which make for wholeness, reflecting the value of his life, and sharing in the power which augments it.

The physical world silently imposes its trust upon us, and waits to be adopted by us. It awaits adoption in the sense of being treated as part of ourselves, for it is by participation in our inner experience that it receives its own interiority and status. To endow the outer world with inner fervor is to grant a dimension of inwardness to matter and a new shape to the world. The Gospel describes this kind of "adoption" in the parable of the Good Samaratin form.[38] An object lies inert and nameless by the wayside. Passing travelers scarcely notice it, and this fleeting perception rapidly fades from their minds. But one man focuses his attention upon it, and his looking is an act of self-forgetful concentration upon that which meets his gaze. He does not consider whether his immediate experience is painful or pleasant, objectively real or hallucinatory, expected or unexpected, like or unlike that which has confronted others. He does not ask whether this is the beginning of an act of love on his part toward his neighbor, or an occasion for doing good; for all these considerations would disrupt his attention and divert his thinking away from the object and toward himself. To imagine himself loving something for the sake of God, or reflecting that what he was about to do pleased God, would kill the creativity of the moment; even these reflections would deprive the object of inwardness, and have the effect of abandoning it in the scale of being at the level of a useful or promising piece of matter. Such is the moment's sensitivity that under the impact of a single thought of God it would be destroyed!

Inasmuch as things are observed creatively in an act of self-renunciation, one man readily exposes himself and sees with a sacrificial eye. The moment of creative attention commands him completely; he has all he can do to concentrate upon the wayside object, to be diminished by the expenditure of energy such looking requires, and to be so far removed from himself as to become unaware of his own existence. This moment of renunciation is one in which the calculations of self-interest are all supplanted by engagement with his immediate environment. He bestows upon the object an inwardness which lifts it up and grants it a share in his life. And the actions which follow reveal the creativity of his attentive glance, for the inert, anonymous object is raised to freedom and a life of its own; indeed, under the eye of rescuing love, the object acquires personal characteristics. It becomes a person!

In a moment of compassionate attention, things acquire a

quality of existence which they did not previously possess. Being loved for their own sakes, they inherit a share of man's freedom. Of course, the earth will not develop human characteristics or be endowed with human feelings, though it may cease to be "real estate." It is granted a value in itself; its existence is promoted; and in the same movement the humanity of its promoter is enhanced.

It seems, therefore, despite the false emphases or terrible neglects of orthodox Christianity, that Biblical interest in the unity of mankind and the world as the condition of personal life, and its vision of cosmic redemption, witness to the place of the natural world in the society of man, and in so doing communicate to each reciprocally its awaited freedom.

NOTES

1. *Science,* March 10, 1967, Vol. 155, No. 3767, pp. 1203–7.
2. *Song of Solomon,* 5:10–16.
3. *Job,* chapters 38ff.
4. *Psalms,* 104.
5. *Hosea,* 2:21–22 (R.S.V.).
6. *Psalms,* 26:2.
7. *Job,* 6:30.
8. *Job,* 38:36 (A.V.).
9. *Psalms,* 6:4.
10. *Isaiah,* 3:20.
11. cf. *Numbers,* 16:1–35; *Joshua,* 7:24–25.
12. *Job,* 31:38–40.
13. *Genesis,* 24:66.
14. *Jeremiah,* 1:9.
15. cf. *Isaiah,* 2:1.
16. *Isaiah,* 2:3.
17. *Jeremiah,* 20:9.
18. *Proverbs,* 8: 22–27, 30.
19. I *John,* 1:1.
20. *John,* 1:4 (New English Bible).

21. *Amos,* 4:6–13.
22. I *Enoch,* 45:5.
23. *Isaiah,* 11:6–9.
24. *Ezekiel,* 34: 25–30.
25. *Hosea,* 2: 18–23.
26. *Revelation,* 5:13 (New English Bible).
27. *Mark,* 2: 9–12.
28. *Colossians,* 1:15–20.
29. *Ephesians,* 1:10.
30. *John,* 1:3–4.
31. *Romans,* 8:21.
32. Pierre Teilhard de Chardin: *Hymn of the Universe* (New York: Harper, 1965), p. 24.
33. *On the Sacred Liturgy.* Encyclical Letter (Mediator Dei) of Pope Pius XII, November 20, 1947 (New York: The America Press, 1954) §20 and §131.
34. *Genesis,* 1:26.
35. *Romans,* 8:19.
36. II *Corinthians,* 5:17.
37. *The Need for Roots* (London: Routledge & Kegan Paul, 1952), p. 91.
38. *Luke,* 10: 30–35.

ABOUT THE AUTHORS

ABOUT THE AUTHORS

MICHAEL HAMILTON was born in Belfast, Ireland. After service in the British Army he emigrated to Canada, where he first worked in a retail business. He received his B.A. from the University of Toronto and his B.D. from Virginia Theological School. Canon Hamilton was ordained in the Episcopal Church, and in 1955 began his ministry living in a tenement slum in Cincinnati. He then spent six years at the University of Southern California as Episcopal Chaplain to Faculty and Graduate Students. Since 1964 he has been on the staff at the National Cathedral in Washington, D.C., where he is responsible for organizing conferences and programs exploring the relation of the Christian faith to changes in the secular culture. Canon Hamilton is editor of *The Vietnam War—Christian Perspectives* (Eerdmans, 1967). In 1956, he married Sarah Glidden Clippinger. They have two children.

PAUL B. SEARS, born in Ohio in 1891, has had a lifelong interest and career in conservation. He received his bachelor's degree from Ohio Wesleyan, his master's degree from Nebraska, and his doctorate from Chicago. His special field of interest is ecology and its application in the management of natural resources, in the history of vegetation, and in land-use planning. Professor Sears has served as president of the American Association for the Advancement of Science, of the Ecological Society of America, and of the American Society of Naturalists, and as chairman of the board of the National Audubon Society. He has also taught in a number of American universities. Until his retirement, he was Professor of Conservation at Yale University.

In addition to numerous articles of both technical and general interest, he has written nearly a dozen books on environmental problems, the last two being *The Living Landscape* (Basic Books, 1966) and *Lands Beyond the Forest* (Prentice-Hall, 1969).

In his opening chapter, Professor Sears with characteristic vividness portrays both the emergence and the recognition of conservation problems in this country. He has had firsthand experience with many of the conditions which he describes.

WILLIAM G. POLLARD received his doctorate in physics at Rice University in 1935 and began his academic career as professor of physics at the University of Tennessee. He received a leave of absence in 1944 to work on the Manhattan Project as a research scientist. In 1947 he was appointed executive director of the Oak Ridge Associated Universities in Tennessee, where he presently works. Dr. Pollard has received a number of honorary degrees and awards besides serving as chairman of the Southeastern section of the American Physical Society, as Fellow of the American Physical Society, of the American Association for the Advancement of Science, and of the American Nuclear Society. He served as trustee of the University of the South, and has taught in the graduate school of theology there.

In mid-career Dr. Pollard began studies in theology, and in 1954 he was ordained to the priesthood in the Episcopal Church. He has since assisted in the ministry of St. Stephen's Episcopal Church in Oak Ridge, has been active in local and national church conventions, and is a frequent speaker on the religious dimensions of scientific issues.

Among his books are *Chance and Providence* (Scribners, 1958), *Physicist and Christian* (Seabury, 1961), and *Man on a Space Ship* (Claremont College, 1967). In his chapter, his thinking ranges widely over the relationship between God's creation of the earth and modern man's concern for its limited natural resources. He is currently working on an expansion of ideas developed in his chapter into a book-length treatment of a theology of nature and of man's relationship to it.

IVAN L. BENNETT, JR., is a scientist who has worked in both the fields of medicine and of public administration. He received his M.D. from

Emory University in 1946 and his diplomate from the American Board of Internal Medicine in 1954. Although most of his academic life has been associated with the Johns Hopkins University, he has also taught at Emory and Yale. Dr. Bennett has been a consultant in a variety of medical assignments, research director for numerous projects, a lecturer, and the author of over a hundred articles on medical matters.

In 1966, Dr. Bennett became the deputy director of the Office of Science and Technology at the Executive Office of the President, where he served as chairman of the Panel on the World Food Supply. This panel contributed volume one of *The World Food Problem, A Report of the President's Science Advisory Committee.*

In 1969, he moved to New York to serve as vice-president for health affairs at New York University and also as director of its medical center. He is presently devoting his time to problems of health care for the disadvantaged and to the field of disarmament.

In this chapter, Dr. Bennett provides a summary of the complex forces impinging on the world's food-population equation.

ROGER L. SHINN studied theology at Union Theological Seminary and received his doctorate in philosophy from Columbia University. He was ordained a minister in the Evangelical and Reformed Church in 1946. After service in the Second World War, he taught in the Department of Philosophy at Heidelberg College and then as Professor of Theology and Christian Ethics at Vanderbilt University Divinity School. He is presently Professor of Applied Christianity at Union Theological Seminary and Adjunct Professor of Religion at Columbia University.

His particular interest has been in the field of social ethics, but he has also lectured and written widely in the field of Christian faith and current affairs. Dr. Shinn is author of many books, including *Christianity and the Problem of History* (Scribners, 1953), *The Existentialist—A Posture* (Association Press, 1959), *Tangled World* (Scribners, 1965), and *Man: The New Humanism* (Westminster Press, 1968).

In addition, he has been active in issues of social justice, has served on the Committee for Racial Justice Now of the United

Church of Christ, has been a consultant for the World Council of Churches and chairman of the Committee on Church and Economic Life of the Council of Churches. He is currently working on ethical issues in genetic experimentation and ecology.

In this chapter, Dr. Shinn explores the motivations and inhibitions relating to family size as well as the ethical implications of these factors.

CLARENCE J. GLACKEN received his A.B. from the University of California in Berkeley and his Ph.D. from Johns Hopkins University in 1951. At present he is professor and chairman of the Department of Geography at the University of California, Berkeley. His particular interests have been cultural geography; that is, the relations between nature and culture, and the history of geographic ideas. Professor Glacken has attended a number of international symposiums on environmental and conservation issues, and has traveled as a Fulbright research scholar to Norway. In 1965, he received a Guggenheim Fellowship.

In addition to numerous articles, he has written two books, including the classic work *Traces on the Rhodian Shore—Nature and Culture in Western Thought from Ancient Times to the End of the Eighteenth Century* (University of California, 1967). He is currently working on a sequel to this work describing developments in Western thought relating to culture and environment during the nineteenth and twentieth centuries.

In this chapter, Professor Glacken shows the rising concern among Western scholars as they begin to understand the vastness of the ecological damage done by age-old practices and industrialization.

CONRAD BONIFAZI was born in England in 1912 and received his B.A. in theology from the University of Bristol in 1944. He also studied in Geneva under a World Council of Churches scholarship and earned his M.A. in 1950 for a thesis comparing Kierkegaard with Nietzsche. He has written three books, including *A Theology of Things* (Lippincott, 1967), which was a study of man in his physical environment; he was subsequently awarded the degree of Doctor of Divinity by the Pacific University in Oregon in 1968.

After service as a young man in the Swiss Alpine Infantry, he returned to England, where he was ordained in the Congregational Church and served in pastorates there. In 1963, Dr. Bonifazi became Associate Professor of Philosophy of Religion at the Pacific School of Religion in Berkeley, California, where he still teaches. He has served on a number of commissions and societies in England, the European continent, and more recently in the United States; he is presently working on a history of the idea of the liveliness of matter.

In this final chapter, Dr. Bonifazi provides a fresh Biblical perspective on the relation between man and his environment.